# A Neutron
## Walks into a Bar...

# A Neutron Walks into a Bar...

## Random Facts About Our Universe and Everything in It

Compiled by Aoibhinn Ní Shúilleabháin, Maria Delaney,
Humphrey Jones & Paul O'Dwyer

HACHETTE
BOOKS
IRELAND

First published in 2012 by Hachette Books Ireland
First published in paperback in 2013 by Hachette Books Ireland
A division of Hachette UK Ltd.

*Contributors to Science140 via Twitter or the website have agreed to allow the publication
of their tweets without any payment and forego any claim or copyright. Acknowledgement
will be attributed in the final publication. The authors regret any accidental omissions from
acknowledgement. Not all tweets will be published. Publication profits will go directly to research
funded by the Cystic Fibrosis Association of Ireland. The scientific facts, information and advice
in this book have come from private individuals. The authors and publishers have endeavoured
to check and verify all facts to the best of their ability but take no responsibility for advice or
experiments contained herein.*

A CIP catalogue record for this title is available from the British Library.

ISBN  978 1444 74374 6

Book design and typesetting by Anú Design, Tara
Cover design by Anú Design, Tara

Printed and bound in Great Britain by Clays Ltd, St Ives, plc.

Hachette Books Ireland policy is to use papers that are natural, renewable and recyclable
products and made from wood grown in sustainable forests. The logging and manufacturing
processes are expected to conform to the environmental regulations of the country of origin.

Hachette Books Ireland
A Castlecourt Centre

338 Euston Road
London NW1

# *Preface*

The inspiration for this book came from an encounter on the social media platform Twitter. In February 2012, Aoibhinn Ní Shúilleabháin tweeted a description of a glo-stick's chemical reactions in the 140-character limit allowed by Twitter. On reading the tweet, Paul O'Dwyer suggested that encapsulating scientific thoughts, principles and concepts in 140 characters could prove challenging for the online scientific community! Humphrey Jones concurred, and set about constructing a medium through which we could test this #Science140 theory, while Maria Delaney was drafted to help co-ordinate the @Science140 Twitter account and website. An open invitation was extended to all online to participate in our little experiment.

The worlds of nanotechnology, zoology, the universe and even science jokes were among the many daily themes explored over the three months that followed. Thousands of #Science140 tagged tweets, each explaining a scientific fact, principle or definition, were submitted by science enthusiasts worldwide. We have collated the best of them here for you to enjoy.

One scientific fact that was of interest to us was that Ireland has the highest incidence of Cystic Fibrosis in the world. To this end, all proceeds from the sale of this book are being donated to scientific research into Cystic Fibrosis.

The book you hold in your hand is about science but is for everyone. The crowdsourcing nature of the contributions means that scientists and science enthusiasts from every corner of the globe helped create it.

We hope you enjoy reading this book. We have certainly enjoyed putting it together.

*Aoibhinn Ní Shuilleabháin, Maria Delaney,*
*Humphrey Jones and Paul O'Dwyer*

# WHAT IS SCIENCE?

The word 'science' comes from the Latin word *scientia*, meaning knowledge.

Science is the systematic gathering of knowledge based on testable explanations and predictions formed by observing the world around us!

It's also the subject everyone avoided at school, except the weird kids.

A scientific theory is 'something that is disprovable, but has yet to be disproved'.

Science: Get curious, gather data, spot patterns, make predictions, test, confirm or deny, use knowledge to make the world better.

Science = observation → hypothesis → prediction → test → evaluation of hypothesis.

Science = the key to every 'cool', 'awesome', 'wow', 'look – at – that', 'how does that work?', 'what is the difference between this and that?' of a kid.

Science is the best description of the universe we have at any one time. It is continually refined and changed to be better.

# THE UNIVERSE!

 The universe is thought to have begun with the Big Bang approximately 13.7 billion years ago.

 The Big Bang is the theory of the evolution of the universe. It happened everywhere and is expanding.

 The Big Bang was not a 'bang', big or small or any other size. There was nothing in which it could go 'bang'.

 Both space and time came into existence at the Big Bang – it makes no sense to ask the question of what came before it.

 The fundamental forces of physics were in place by $10^{-11}$ seconds. At $10^{-6}$ seconds, protons and neutrons emerged.

 At a few minutes, some protons and neutrons merged into deuterium and helium nuclei; most protons stayed as hydrogen nuclei.

But it was another 379,000 years before electrons combined with protons to form atoms, mostly of hydrogen.

 The only elements produced in the Big Bang were hydrogen, helium and lithium. Every other element has been 'made' since.

 Most of the atoms in your body were created in stars through fusion. You are a way for the universe to know itself.

 96% of the universe is dark energy and dark matter, which won't interact with you. The universe is mostly antisocial.

 The universe is currently enjoying its Stelliferous Era, and this era will continue for another 100 trillion years.

 Dark matter is invisible material thought to make up about 23% of the content of the cosmos. It has never been detected directly.

 Space is a seething mass of particles and antiparticles appearing and annihilating each other. Including near black holes.

# Star facts

A shooting star is a demonstration of our atmosphere protecting us. Friction causes heat which burns up most meteorites.

The most luminous known star is R136a1 in the Large Magellanic Cloud. It's 8.7 million times brighter than the Sun!

The oldest known star is HE 1523-0901. At 13.2 billion years old, it's almost as old as the universe itself!

A brown dwarf is a 'failed star'. Not massive enough to fuse hydrogen, but more massive than a giant planet.

The Sun is our closest star!

# The Sun is HOT!

✳ The surface temperature of the Sun (our closest star) is 5,600°C. Its core is about 15 million°C!

✳ In 5 billion years, our sun will become a red giant, swallowing at least Mercury and Venus. Life on Earth will be gone.

✳ The Sun's magnetic field is very strong and very complicated. Its magnetosphere (or heliosphere) extends well beyond Pluto!

✳ Light (photons) takes 8 minutes 22 seconds to reach Earth from the surface of the Sun but 100,000 years from its core.

# OUR SOLAR SYSTEM!

- A solar system consists of one or more stars and all the bodies that orbit the star's, or multiple stars', common centre of gravity.

- The estimated time it takes our solar system to complete an orbit of our galaxy is between 200 and 250 million Earth years.

- **M**ary's **V**irgin **E**xplanation **M**ade **J**oseph **S**uspect **U**pstairs **N**eighbour
  *Mercury, Venus, Earth, Mars, Jupiter, Saturn, Uranus, Neptune*

- Pluto is not a planet anymore.

- The Sun contains 99.86% of all the mass of the solar system.

- The most Earth-like conditions in the solar system are, surprisingly, on Venus, just above the cloud decks.

- At Venus' surface, the pressure is so great that carbon dioxide in its atmosphere is no longer a gas, but a supercritical fluid.

- The cause of Venus' sulphuric acid clouds is unknown, but they would disappear if they weren't being replenished somehow.

- As well as Mars, the possibility of solar-system life has been discussed on Titan, Europa, Enceladus, Io, Venus and Jupiter!

- Due to its orbit, Pluto has the most dramatic seasonal changes in the solar system, which reshape its entire surface!

- All planets rotate. In the time it takes you to read this, the Earth will spin you 1,500 metres.

- Pluto has not been seen since it went off in a huff after being demoted out of planet club in 2006.

OUR SOLAR SYSTEM!

# The Moon

 Moon – a natural planetary satellite, the name of Earth's natural satellite or the act of exposing one's buttocks suddenly.

The Moon is thought to be about 40 million years younger than Earth and the result of a collision with it.

Because of low gravity, geological features on the Moon are larger than on Earth. Everest-sized mountains are not uncommon there! ⇨

Never host a party on the moon – no atmosphere

Maximum walking speed is set by gravity. That's why it's better to bounce than to walk on the moon.

 The Moon not only orbits the Earth, but the Earth also orbits the moon.

 Moon dust feels like snow and smells like gunpowder. It is mostly silicon dioxide glass created by meteors hitting the moon.

 The surface area of the moon is 14,658,000 square miles or 9.4 billion acres!

 When Alan Shepard was on the moon, he hit a golf ball and drove it 730 metres (or nearly half a mile).

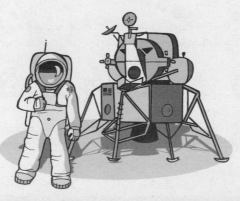

# Earth is home...
## it's also pretty cool!

 Earth has a mass of approximately 600,000,000,000,000,000,000,000,000 kilograms. In other words, it's quite heavy.

 Nearly half the atoms that make up everything on planet Earth are oxygen atoms.

 The Earth is not really round. It is called an oblate spheroid meaning it's slightly flattened at the poles.

 In fact, Earth's radius is 22 kilometres shorter at the poles than the equator. That's more than Mount Everest.

 Earth is the only known world capable of supporting intelligent life. Whether or not it does support intelligent life is debatable.

Earth is the only planet in the solar system not to be named after a mythical god.

 Earth is the only planet to have water in three states of matter: solid in ice, liquid in sea, rain etc. and gas in clouds.

 6,900 languages have been defined on our planet, most of which are spoken by groups of 1,000 people (or fewer).

 We get 3,000 times more heat from the Sun than we do from the centre of the Earth.

 The Earth is actually nearer to the Sun in the winter (in the northern hemisphere) than in the summer.

 The deepest mine on Earth is a goldmine in South Africa at 4 kilometres. It has a temp of 60°C cooled to 30°C by ice so miners can work there. It takes 1 hour to reach it!

 The average temperature on Earth is +14°C because of presence of carbon dioxide in atmosphere, otherwise should be −18°C.

# Stuff we don't really Need to know ...

The Wikipedia entry on 'Toilet roll orientation' contains more words than the 'Biology' entry!

Crows can recognise and memorise human faces. They are also one of the few birds to use tools to obtain food.

An army ant swarm can cross water by arranging themselves into a large rotating ball.

---->

Camels are amazing! They've oval blood cells to enable them to drink huge amounts of water in a short time. If we tried, we'd die!

Clownfish undergo sequential hermaphroditism. After Nemo's mum gets eaten Nemo's dad would have become a female.

# Baby, It's Better Down Where's It's Wetter ...

Oceans cover 70% of the Earth's surface.
More than 90% of the planet's living biomass
is found in the oceans.

✳✳✳

There are 5 oceans, 113 seas and 165 major rivers
in the world harbouring a wide diversity of life!

✳✳✳

More than 3.5 billion people depend on the ocean
for their primary source of food. In 20 years, this
number could double!

✳✳✳

$CaCO_3$ (calcium carbonate) is an unusual compound in
that more of it dissolves at lower temperatures –
so deep ocean currents transport a lot of it.

✳✳✳

The Mariana Trench (North Pacific Ocean) is the
deepest location on Earth (maximum depth 10,911
metres). The pressure at the bottom is 108.6MPa.
Apparently, that's like a person holding up 50 jumbo jets.

The oceans are an enormous carbon sink, storing approximately ¼ of the world's carbon. Shifting sea temperatures may drastically change this.

✳✳✳

Scientists have estimated that the number of undiscovered species in the ocean could be from 750,000 to 2.2 million!

✳✳✳

Belize is the country with the second longest coral barrier reef in the world. The longest belongs to Australia.

✳✳✳

Life began in the seas 3.1 billion to 3.4 billion years ago. Land dwellers appeared 400 million years ago! Fairly recently!

✳✳✳

Around 400 million years ago, the first creatures to set foot on land were probably giant sea scorpions.

✳✳✳

There are trenches, volcanoes and entire mountain ranges underneath the ocean!

Mysterious low-frequency sounds have been recorded in the deep Pacific the source of which remains unknown.

✱✱✱

A hydrothermal vent is when two plates of the Earth's crust are moving apart under the sea.

✱✱✱

Some people think the first organisms on Earth lived at hydrothermal vents, not as photosynthesising plankton.

✱✱✱

Also, every hydrothermal vent has its own unique species, which are not found anywhere else in the world!

✱✱✱

The ocean floor is Earth's largest habitat – we genuinely do know more about the surface of Mars!

✱✱✱

The eyes of octopus and squid work like ours, but they don't have a blind spot like we do. Convergent evolution in action.

# Water is Weird!

Water is one of the most common, most unusual and most important molecules in the universe all at once.

Hot water can freeze faster than cold water – the Mpemba effect. No one knows why. Maybe it's magic. Or science.

Water is unusual in that its solid state is less dense than its liquid state. It is densest around 4°C.

Super-cooled water: water brought to a temperature below its freezing point that remains in liquid form and doesn't solidify.

Water is made of two atoms of hydrogen and one atom of oxygen, chemically combined using covalent bonding.

Water has a boiling point of 100°C and a freezing point of 0°C.

Snowflakes form their starry shapes because each molecule of water is angular. The solid builds up along axes of these angles.

A vapour cloud with 140 trillion times more water than Earth's oceans has been detected 12 billion light years away in a quasar.

Water, the third most abundant molecule in the universe, is a combination of the first and third most abundant elements, hydrogen and oxygen.

The largest single reservoir of water in the solar system is Europa, containing over twice as much water as the Earth's oceans.

# No Jokes
## about Potassium ... K

I tried to study
the history of the
Periodic Table ...
I found it such a Bohr.

The astrophysicists always
promised the best parties ...
claiming they'd be
'out of this world'.

How many moles are
in a guacamole?
Avocado's number.

Why does a burger have lower energy than a steak? Because it's in the ground state.

If I could be any enzyme, I'd be a DNA helicase *sleazy look*, so I could unzip your genes *wink*.

Why are bacteria bad at maths? Because they multiply by dividing.

Why did the bear dissolve in water? Because it was a polar bear!

# Extreme Animals

The animals said to hear the lowest sounds are elephants and ferrets (12Hz) whilst beluga whales can hear the highest (120KHz!).

A dog has over 220 million olfactory receptors in its nose. Humans have just 5 million! So why do they sniff such disgusting things?

Some snakes are still lethal up to an hour after they have had their heads cut off.

The pistol shrimp's claw has evolved into a gun, able to stun/kill fish with a fluid shockwave.

The shockwave from the pistol shrimp's claw also generates temperatures hotter than the sun's surface, through cavitation!

Vampire bats don't suck blood – they make an incision and lap it up like cats. But if your cat does this get help.

Wolverines have been known to attack bears, animals about 20 times their size. And it's not defence, actual unprovoked attacks.

The Mississippi alligator can stay under water (without breathing that is) for 6 hours!

# Strange Animal Behaviour!

Rats can't vomit, they have no gag reflex. For an animal that eats so much filth yet is still so numerous, that's quite amazing.

Frogs don't vomit either. They invert their stomachs out of their mouths, use their hands to clean them out and then re-swallow them.

In order to eat, starfish eject their stomach from their bodies and envelop their food. I'm sure you can think of people who do that too.

# Random Stuff Walks into a Bar ...

Hydrogen atom walks into a bar.
'Someone just stole my electron!'
Barman: 'Are you sure?'
H Atom: 'Yes, I'm positive!'

A proton walks into a bar.
Barman asks, 'How are you?'
Proton says, 'Well, up and down. And up.'

A neutron walks into a bar, orders
a beer, and asks, 'How much?'
Barman says, 'For you, no charge.'
Boom, boom!

A virus walks into a bar, barman says,
'We don't serve virus in here.'
The virus replies, 'Well, you're not a
very good host.'

'We don't allow faster than light neutrinos in here,' said the bartender.

A neutrino walks into a bar.

A horse walks into a bar, the barman asks, 'Why the long face?'
The horse replies, 'Evolutionary selective pressures.'

Schrödinger's cat walks into a bar and doesn't.

All the noble gases walk into a bar. No reaction.

A man walks into a bar: 'I'd like a molecule used for intracellular energy transfer please.'
Barman: 'That'll be 80p.'

# Wise Words from the Masters

'Anyone not shocked
by quantum mechanics has
not yet understood it.'
*Niels Bohr*

'The difference between stupidity and genius
is that genius has its limits.'
*Albert Einstein*

'If I have a thousand ideas and only one
turns out to be good, I am satisfied.'
*Alfred Nobel*

'The science of today is the technology
of tomorrow.'
*Edward Teller*

'Knowledge is the food of the soul.'
*Plato*

'Gravitation is not responsible for people
falling in love.'
*Albert Einstein*

'If I have seen further than others, it is by
standing upon the shoulders of giants.'
*Isaac Newton*

'A physicist is just an atom's
way of looking at itself.'
*Niels Bohr*

'Equipped with his five senses, man explores
the universe around him and calls the
adventure Science.'
*Edwin Hubble*

'Science is a wonderful thing if one does not
have to earn one's living at it.'
*Albert Einstein*

'No great discovery was ever made
without a bold guess.'
*Isaac Newton*

# Amazing Plants

The Venus Flytrap needs to 'eat' flies because it grows on nutrient-poor soil. Each trap has 6 hairs, triggered by being moved twice.

Nutmeg is very poisonous if injected intravenously.

Kurkara, the Australian Desert Oak, drops its needles forming a fireproof circle around its base and so survives bush fires.

Trees can lose several hundred gallons of water a day through transpiration. At the peak of water loss, their trunks get thinner.

Relaxed plants just go with the phloem!

Pineapples contain an enzyme (bromelin) that breaks down proteins. It's a fruit that eats you back!

The pineapple enzyme is the reason you may get a numb tongue while eating it and why pineapple pickers lose their fingerprints.

There are nearly 1,000 types of carnivorous plants on record. When they reach 4-figures, the botanic rebellion will begin …

From foxglove to treat heart disease, to willow as a source of aspirin, around 25% of medicines are derived from plants.

There is a plant that is deadly if you sit under it for 10 minutes. It is called a water lily.

The lotus flower has nano features on its surface making it 'self-cleaning' or hydrophobic. You can also see this on cabbage leaves.

# WHAT'S A MOLE?

## (SCIENCE CAN BE CONFUSING TOO!)

A mole is the amount of pure substance containing the same number of chemical units as there are atoms in exactly 12 grams of carbon-12.

A mole is a small furry creature that likes to burrow underground. It has very sharp spade-like claws and is nearly blind.

A mole is a long-term spy who is recruited before he has access to secret intelligence, and works undercover in the target.

Mole is the generic name for a number of sauces used in Mexican cuisine.

A mole is a benign tumour on human skin, usually with darker pigment.

A mole is a massive structure, usually of stone, used as a pier, breakwater or causeway between places separated by water.

# SMALL
# SCIENCE

The smallest bacteria are called mycoplasma and, unlike most, they lack a cell wall. They are approximately 0.1 microns ($\mu$m) in size ...

0.1$\mu$m is too small to be seen by a standard light microscope, but can wreak havoc on cell cultures, so we try to test for them.

Bacteriophages (bacteria-eating viruses) invade specific bacteria that are tricked into making new viruses and bursting open.

The largest known viruses are actually larger, and have longer genomes, than some types of bacteria.

'Deinococcus radiodurans' is the world's toughest bacterium. It can survive cold, dehydration, acid, vacuum and radiation.

It's the Chuck Norris of bacteria! Some people have nicknamed it Conan the Bacterium!

# SMALLER

# SCIENCE

# -NANO !

The word 'nano' comes from the Greek word 'nanos' meaning 'dwarf', it is a billionth of a metre or $10^{-9}$.

Nanotechnology is the study of manipulating matter on an atomic and molecular scale.

Nanotechnology: science, engineering and technology conducted at the nanoscale, 1–100 nanometres.

1 nanometre is about 100,000 times smaller than the width of one hair on your head – or about 4 to 5 atoms wide.

A nanometre is $1 \times 10^{-9}$ which is 0.000000001 metres.

The size of a nanometre to a metre is the same as a marble to the size of the Earth.

Your fingernail grows 1 nanometre every second.

Plain English definition: 1 nanometre is the amount a man's beard grows in the time it takes him to lift a razor to his face.

Nanotechnology has been around longer than we knew. One of the widest-used applications is in the photocatalyst in sunscreen.

Nanoparticles have really unusual properties because of their tiny size and their comparatively large surface area.

One of the most promising nanomaterials is graphene (a thin material that makes up graphite – the lead in most pencils).

Graphene is a one-atom-thick layer of carbon atoms.

We can now make long tubes out of these sheets of carbon, over 1 million times long as wide. These have many possible uses.

Carbon atoms are like octopuses with four free hands each, so can join to four other carbon atoms at once, making a sheet.

It takes tens of thousands of carbon nanotubes to make up the width of a human hair!

Carbon nanotubes are the strongest, stiffest materials known to man.

# Bright Sparks

## Famous Scientists!

* Ernest Walton (1903–1995):
  Ireland's only science Nobel Laureate.
  Helped build first successful particle
  accelerator. Split the atom!

  George Boole (1815–1864):
  Professor of Maths at University College Cork
  and inventor of Boolean Logic. The internet
  and Twitter would not exist without him!

  Beatrix Potter (1866–1943):
  Thwarted scientist, discovered that lichens
  are actually two organisms (alga and fungus)
  living symbiotically.

Florence Nightingale (1820–1910):
The first woman elected to fellowship
of the Royal Statistical Society.

Carl Linnaeus (1707–1778):
Swedish botanist who proposed the modern
system of biological nomenclature.
Published *Systema Naturae*.

Marie Curie (1867–1934):
Nobel Prize-winning physicist and chemist,
researched radioactivity, died in
1934 as a result of her pioneering work.

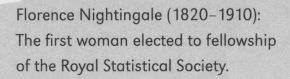

More on Marie Curie:
She discovered two elements and was the
first person to be awarded two Nobel prizes!

Enrico Fermi (1901–1954):
Nobel Prize-winning physicist known for the development of the first nuclear reactor.

Linus Pauling (1901–1994):
Double Nobel Prize winner, chemist, biochemist, pioneer of quantum chemistry.

Caroline Herschel (1750–1848):
Discovered several comets and in particular the periodic comet 35P/Herschel-Rigollet, which bears her name.

Dr Bunsen Honeydew (1976–):
Scientist and communicator who overcame his lack of eyes to excel in his field. Inventor of the Gorilla Detector.

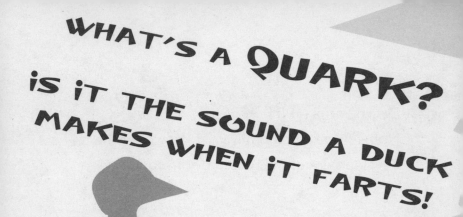

# WHAT'S A QUARK? iS iT THE SOUND A DUCK MAKES WHEN iT FARTS!

You know why helium
makes you laugh?
Get a few of them together
and it's He He, He He.

Male magnets believe female
magnets are repulsive from
behind, but more attractive
from the front.

Quantum physicists
make poor lovers.
When they find position,
they've no momentum
and when they've
momentum, they've
no position.

How many
astronomers does it take
to change a lightbulb?
None – we like sitting
in the dark.

What happens when a body
is immersed in water?
The telephone rings.

# More on the Moon

 The Moon is about 380,000 kilometres away, but still causes the tides on Earth!

 We think our Moon was created when two planets smashed together. The other one involved was a young Earth.

The Moon is not made of cheese!

The Moon does have an iron core, much smaller than the Earth's. It's not quite in the centre but nearer Earth due to gravity.

The Moon always shows the same face to the Earth. It rotates at exactly the same speed as it circles the Earth.

The Moon's orbit is elliptical, some-times closer or farther. A full moon, when it's closest, can be 14% larger than when farthest.

⇨

An eclipse is an event where the Sun's light gets blocked by the Moon or Earth.

Total eclipses only occur because of the fluke coincidence that the sun is 400 times larger than the Moon and also 400 times farther from Earth!

Our Moon used to be much nearer and cause much larger tides. It's still creeping away – total eclipses will cease to exist one day.

People used to think that the Moon could lead to insanity in some people, hence the term 'lunatic' (now disproved of).

# Da Dum, Da Dum, Da Dum, Da Dum, Da Dum!

# SHARK!

The smallest shark at 15.24 centimetres is the male dwarf lantern shark. The largest shark (also the largest fish) is the whale shark.

Evidence for the existence of sharks dates back 420–450 million years. Most modern sharks can be traced back approximately 100 million years!

Sharks are the ultimate example of successful evolution. Their basic design hasn't changed over millions of years!

Sharks don't need dentists. Their teeth grow throughout their lives, so lost or broken ones are simply replaced.

Humans have a much greater chance of being struck by lightning than attacked by sharks. This is because humans live on land.

Shark skin has tiny, tooth-like structures called 'dermal denticles'. It makes them swim faster – the same idea is used in hull and swimsuit design.

Some shark species are able to detect one part per million of blood in sea water.

Sharks can detect electrical fields. They do this through special gel-filled pores in their snout called ampullae of Lorenzini.

In fact, sharks have up to 8 senses – the 5 human ones plus electroperception, pressure sensation and lateral line (sense of vibrations made by prey).

# What's Your Favourite Element?

**Oxygen:** Toxic to most primitive life forms, $O_2$ paved our way of life. Now, here we stand, and breathe.

**Helium:** Without it, the sun won't shine and never will we know the fun of the screeching voice after inhaling it. Also vital in MRI machines.

**Carbon:** The element at the heart of organic chemistry and therefore of life itself. Also forms diamonds, graphite and graphene.

Lead poisoning causes red blood cells to get covered in telltale polka dots – nasty.

Give it up for silicon! Without it, no land to stand on, no super computer, no ubiquitous plastic augmentation surgery.

Hooray for the best threesome of all! Two hydrogen and an oxygen. More than 4.5 billion years together, the parents of life.

**Copper:** Key element in the protein haemocyanin, the oxygen carrier of most molluscs and some arthropods, giving rise to blue blood.

Copper and tellurium, because they're CuTe together!

**Deadly Plutonium, atomic number 94:**
Used in electricity generation! Popular with megalomaniacs for use in nuclear weapons and poison.

**Arsenic:** A highly poisonous metallic element used in insecticides, weed killers, solid-state doping agents and various alloys. Nasty!

Iron has nothing to do with irony. Which, given the name ...

Au. Gold! (Gold!) Spandau Ballet sang about it, so it must be good!

# Regular Magnetism

A magnet has two poles. 'North' N pole is attracted to the 'south' S pole of another magnet. N N poles and S S poles are repulsive.

Not all metals are magnetic! There are only 3 naturally occurring magnetic materials: iron, nickel and cobalt.

Magnetism is more important than you might think. Earth's magnetic field keeps us from getting third-degree sunburn every day.

This is because the sun emits much more than radiation. Our magnetic field shields us from being bombarded by particles.

The strength of a magnet is called its flux density. It's defined as the amount of flux per unit area (units are teslas).

Typical strengths are: Earth's magnetic field (equator) = 31μT, refrigerator magnet = 5 mT, sunspots = 0.3T and MRI scanner = 1.5T to 3T.

Naturally occurring magnets were formed when lightning struck magnetite on Earth!

Magnetite is a ferrimagnetic mineral with chemical formula $Fe_3O_4$.

Magnets can be demagnetised by heating, passing an alternating current through them or by beating them up with a hammer!

# Animal Magnetism!

Magnetoception is the sense that enables an animal to detect a magnetic field to find its direction, altitude or location.

Birds (e.g. pigeons) navigate using magnetoception via a mineral embedded in their brains called magnetite.

Magnetite is also found in the human nose, suggesting that we may have once had magnetoception, but have now 'forgotten' it.

Robins can see magnetic fields, but only with their right eye. I can't help picturing eye-patched robins going, 'Aaarrr!'

Magnetotactic bacteria contain magnetosomes that enable them to migrate along the Earth's magnetic field lines.

The subterranean Zambian mole rat uses magnetoreception to orient itself in its underground nest.

# We're Hopping Mad about Frogs!

Did you know frogs outlived the dinosaurs! They're tougher than they look!

The earliest modern frog (Sanyanlichan) is from about 125 million years ago (late Jurassic era).

Frogs don't drink water using their mouths – they absorb it using their skin.

Frogs are in the order Anura, along with toads.

Our common separation of frogs from toads is not supported by taxonomy! End the discrimination!

Sometimes only male frogs croak. Each species has its own unique sound. Some aren't croaks – some whistle, some chirp like a bird.

A group of frogs is called an 'army' as opposed to a 'knot' of toads.

The first frog in space went up in March 1961 with the Soviet Vostok 3A flights. One small hop for frog ...

*Paedophryne amauensis* is the world's smallest frog, measuring just 7.9 millimetres from head to tail, making it no bigger than a house fly.

You could fit three *Paedophryne amauensis* on top of a Smartie!

Wallace's Tree Frog (named after Alfred Russell Wallace) can glide up to 15 metres between trees using its enlarged web feet!

Poisonous frogs are only poisonous because of their diet of insects (e.g. ants and mites that carry poisonous alkaloids).

# PLATYPUS, PLATYPUSES, PLATYPI?

The duck-billed platypus is a mammal that lays eggs – one of only three mammal species that do so.

The male duck-billed platypus has poisonous spurs on its hind legs – probably why they don't do much horse riding.

The duck-billed platypus doesn't have specific mammary glands for breast feeding its young, but rather sweats the milk. Lovely!

# We had a 'dino day'!

Dinosaurs living in the late Mesozoic Period shared their world with turtles, crocodiles, birds, snakes, mammals, flowers and frogs.

Pterosaurs, the flying reptiles of the Mesozoic Period famous for achieving giant sizes, were not dinosaurs.

There is no such thing as Brontosaurus. The correct term is Apotosaurus. The mistake was corrected in 1903, but the name persists.

The heaviest dinosaur was Brachiosaurus at 80 tonnes. It was the equivalent of 17 African elephants, 16 metres tall and 26 metres long!

I love dinosaurs – especially with ketchup. (Birds are dinosaurs.)

What do you call a one-eyed dinosaur? Doyathinkhesaurus?

The dino with the longest name was the dome-headed Micropachycephalosaurus or 'tiny thick-headed lizard'. It was only 17 centimetres tall!

The earliest known truly human ancestor and the oldest known living dinosaur lived roughly 60,000,000 years apart.

Diplodocus had two brains – one in its head, the other in its ass! It was bigger than the T-Rex but an omnivorous, peace and love kind of creature.

The Velociraptor probably had feathers, looking a bit like a chicken. *Jurassic Park* not so scary now, huh?

# SCIENCE
## MNEMONICS!

Two Old Angels, Sitting On High,
Chatting About Heaven (tan, sin, cos).

King Neptune Caught Many Angry Zulus
Fighting Hairy Police Constables Having
Asthma Attacks (Activity Series of Elements
– look it up!)

My Very Excellent Mother Just Served Us
Nachos (The eight planets! It used
to be 'Nine Pizzas' – I like pizza
better).

Gate X Usually Lets In Most
Radiation (Gamma, X-rays, UV, visible
Light, IR, Microwaves and Radio –
starting with smallest wavelength).

Richard Of York Gave Battle In Vain (*the colours of the rainbow —* red, orange, yellow, green, blue, indigo, violet).

Alternative to Richard of York, etc. for colours of the rainbow — Right Over Your Green Blouse I Vomit.

Oil Rig (oxidation is loss, reduction is gain — an oldie but a goodie).

King Philip came over for grouse shooting (Kingdom, Phylum, Class, etc.).

Old People From Texas Eat Spiders (Occipital, Parietal, Frontal, Temporal, Ethnoid, Sphenoid — bones of the skull).

We guarantee certainty, clearly referring to this light mnemonic (for the speed of light — just count the letters in each word).

How I need a drink, alcoholic in nature, after the heavy lectures involving quantum mechanics (first 14 digits of pi — 3.14159265358979).

Only Bad Astronomers Forget Generally Known Mnemonics (stellar classification — look it up, tricky one).

Party Monday, Again Tuesday
(Stages of mitosis — Prophase, Metaphase,
Anaphase and Telophase).

# Computers!

The first computer was invented by Charles Babbage in 1834. The Difference Engine was essentially a mechanical calculator. Respect!

Konrad Zuse's Z3 was the first programmable computer, invented in 1941.

The Colossus computer was the first completely electronic computer – it was used to crack German codes during the Second World War.

By the end of the 1950s, computers were much smaller. Still as big as a double decker bus though.

Mobile phones have far more computing power than Apollo spacecraft. This is irrelevant though, the moon has no network coverage.

A computer is only as intelligent as the person using it. Remember this the next time you abuse it because 'it' made a mistake.

Ada Lovelace is often considered the first computer programmer. Never let it be said women aren't techies!

Computer data is stored in binary form (0 or 1) via mechanisms that have varied from holes in paper tape to (soon) electron spin.

While it took the radio 38 years and the television a short 13 years, it took the internet only 4 years to reach 50 million users!

The average computer user blinks 7 times a minute, less than half the normal rate of 20 (he said, not blinking once).

# The Arctic and Antarctic!

Antarctica is the coldest place on Earth, but is a desert and the danger of sunburn is real.

It rarely snows in Antarctica. It can be classified as a desert because there is less than 25 centimetres of precipitation annually.

Antarctica is also the windiest place on Earth with gusts up to 327 kilometres per hour!

If you sit on the Arctic ice for too long, you can get polaroids.

Arctic comes from the Greek for 'bear'. This is because of the prominence of the constellation Ursa Major or Ursa Minor (Ursa = bear).

Antarctic ice reaches 5 kilometres in depth and contains 70% of the Earth's fresh water. If it all melted, sea levels would rise 50-60 metres!

Antarctica is the fifth biggest continent and 10% of the Earth's land area! Only 2% of the land is not covered in ice!

The Arctic is mostly sea while the Antarctic is mostly land. You could say they're poles apart.

# More Extreme Animals

A lungfish can hibernate for as long as four years!

Mongooses are resistant/immune to snake venom. They don't eat or compete with snakes – they fight them because they're 'there'.

Komodo dragons aren't actually real dragons.

As a walrus' skin blood vessels constrict while in cold water, they can appear almost white in colour when they are swimming.

The largest animal known to have existed is the blue whale (at 190 metric tonnes).

Strongest animal in the world is the rhinoceros beetle. It can lift 850 times its own weight! (Not if I stand on the critter!)

Armadillos, opossums and sloths spend up to 80% of their lives sleeping. I know some teenagers like that.

# KITCHEN SCIENCE

# SCIENCE OUTSIDE

First, write a proposal and a safety statement ...
(only kidding)

Rub a plastic ruler with a jumper. Hold over small pieces of paper – electrostatic charges attract paper to ruler. Physicstastic!

Place some whole milk in a saucer, add a few drops of food dye. Put in a drop of detergent and watch what happens to the fats!

Corn starch and water make a non-Newtonian fluid. Solid when under pressure, liquid otherwise!

Vinegar, baking soda, food colouring – make a homemade volcano!

# THE LAB

Add dark food colouring to water. Then place a white-petalled flower stem into it. Over time, the petals will change colour!

Measure the speed of light with marshmallows and a microwave. The melted blobs are a wavelength apart and multiply by the frequency.

Orange peel contains limonene, a flammable oil that you can use to make a flame thrower! (Probably best not to do this at home!)

# Farts, Sneezes, Poos and Pee!

The average cough comes out of your mouth at 60 miles (96.5 kilometres) per hour! A sneeze can reach up to 100 miles (160 kilometres) per hour.

When you pee, a tiny deposit of urine enters the mouth via the saliva glands. You learn something new every day!

Eating beets can turn urine red, rhubarb can turn it brownish or pinkish and vitamin B2 bright yellow!

Earwax is made from sebum, skin cells from inside the ear and secretions from the cerumenous glands in the outer ear canal.

Earwax has two types: wet and dry. People of northeast Asian descent tend to have dry wax, while people from other regions have wet.

Your stomach needs to produce a new layer of mucus every two weeks or it will digest itself.

If you farted constantly for 6 years and 9 months, the gas produced has the energy of an atom bomb . . . Get eating those beans, mad dictators.

After a vasectomy, sperm degrades in the vas deferens as it cannot otherwise be 'emitted'. So don't worry about where it goes.

# Farts, Sneezes, Poos and Pee! contd.

Mature red blood cells do not contain a nucleus and thus do not contain DNA. Nobody tell *CSI*!

Farts contain the following (odourless) gases (in varying quantities): nitrogen, hydrogen, carbon dioxide, methane and oxygen!

**BooM**

The nasty, fart smell is caused by compounds like skatole, indole, methanethiol, hydrogen sulfide and dimethyl sulphide.

The sound farts make is caused by vibrations of the anal sphincter – you can make a louder noise if you clinch!

If you have your bladder removed, surgeons can make you a new one from your small intestine. It's taking the piss, in a good way.

# Reptiles Rule! (The Earth)

There are more than 8,000 species of reptiles on Earth and they live on every continent except Antarctica (too cold ... wimps!).

∗∗∗

The term 'archosaur' means 'ruling reptile', and includes Dinosauria, Crocodilia, and Pterosauria, among other groups.

∗∗∗

Chameleons mostly change colour to communicate, rather than match their background, as is often suggested.

∗∗∗

The venom glands of snakes are located around the upper jaw.

∗∗∗

Venomous lizards house the venom glands in the lower jaw.

Reticulated pythons hold the record for longest snake. Green anacondas hold the record for heaviest snake.

✱✱✱

Gaboon vipers have the longest fangs of any snake.

✱✱✱

The Black Mamba is reported to grow up to 4.3 metres and can propel itself forward at speeds of up to 20mph (cancels holiday to Africa).

✱✱✱

The Marine Iguana (Amblyrhynchus cristatus), a native to the Galapagos Islands, is the only modern marine lizard.

✱✱✱

Rattlesnakes can still bite after they are dead! Zombies? ... No!

✱✱✱

Boffins think reflexes are triggered by still-active infrared sensors.

✱✱✱

A snake's skull is made up of small, flexible interconnected bones, so they can expand their jaws to eat much larger prey.

✱✱✱

The scales of all snakes are made of keratin, which is the same substance that makes up the hair and fingernails of humans.

Snails, lobsters and spiders have blue blood, the colour comes from the haemocyanin molecule which is copper based.

UK giant house spiders are the fastest-running spiders in the world.

Your fingernails grow at roughly the same speed as the Earth's tectonic plates move. It wouldn't be a very exciting race.

The first surgeons were barbers. Hence the red and white poles (blood and bandages).

# The Weather ... Ugggh!

Luke Howard identified 3 principal cloud types – cumulus, stratus and cirrus. The rest of us saw sheep, angels and dragons.

30°–35° north and south are 'horse latitudes'. The weather could be too calm for sailing ships, and Spanish sailors allegedly threw dead horses overboard.

The wettest place in the world is Mawsynram, India, with an average of 11,870 millimetres of rain per year. Have they never been to Mayo?

The droplets of water that make up fog are so small that it would take 7,000,000,000 of them to make one tablespoonful of water!

The fastest winds on Earth are inside a tornado funnel. Winds here have been recorded at 480 kilometres (300 miles) per hour.

The amount of water held in the atmosphere at any time is enough to produce about 2.5 centimetres of rain over the surface of the Earth!

Hail forms from super-cooled water droplets caught in strong up-draughts. Repeated freeze-thaw cycles cause a layered structure.

Rain falls when moist air is forced upwards (by mountains or another air mass at a front) and water droplets condense out.

Why are the winds not called 'northerlies' and 'southerlies'? Because the Coriolis Effect deflects the winds to the east or west.

Every winter around 1 septillion snowflakes fall from the sky! That's a one with 24 zeros after it!

A moonbow is a rainbow from the light reflected off the moon. A fogbow is a rainbow of the water in fog rather than rain.

A rainbow displays a continuous range of colour but is seen as discrete bands because of the different photoreceptors in human eyes.

The fastest winds in the solar system are found on Neptune, they reach 2,100 kilometres per hour!

# Science Poems

Science is discovery and excitement
It's innovation and refinement
Next door and light years away
Science is everything.

Newton was near a tree;
Fleming, the laboratory;
Watson and Crick in The Eagle,
Darwin on the *Beagle*,
Who's best idea was in the WC?

It's down to excess carbon,
Makes me say beg my pardon,
Mixed with $O_2$,
Can't really blame you,
Burps that were heard from your garden.

On Earth they do fight,
A collection of nations.
In space they share might,
International Space Stations.

I'm friends with many elements,
Though some I wound up hating,
But now I've chosen one for life
All thanks to carbon dating.

700nm is red,
400nm is blue,
Or at least that's how receptors show objects to you.

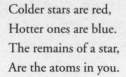

Colder stars are red,
Hotter ones are blue.
The remains of a star,
Are the atoms in you.

Roses are red,
Violets are blue,
I have a rudimentary grasp of botany,
Now you do too.

Pasteur studied germs.
His results were surprising.
He discovered how microbes act.
And is the father of Pasteurising.

# Your DNA is Amazeballs!

Deoxyribonucleic Acid? Well, most people find it easier to pronounce it as DNA.

DNA is found in the nucleus of the cell (those that have them) and also in the mitochondria found in the body of the cell.

Genome: The entirety of an organism's genetic information.

The information held in the DNA molecule is used to code proteins, via a mechanism called transcription.

Proteins are made of chains of amino acids. There are 20 standard amino acids. DNA defines the order and type of amino acid to use.

Gametes (sperm and eggs) only carry half the DNA found in the rest of your cells. Combining sperm and egg makes a full set.

It would take a person typing 60 words a minute, 8 hours a day for around 50 years to type the human genome. You better start now ...

If unwound and tied together the strands of DNA from 1 cell would stretch about 183 centimetres but would be only 125 trillionths of a centimetre wide.

If all the DNA in your body was put end to end, it would reach to the Sun and back over 600 times!

1 million bases (aka a megabase) of DNA sequence data is roughly equivalent to 1 megabyte of computer data storage space!

GM crops have DNA from another organism inserted in them to give them properties (e.g. pest resistance).

The chloroplasts of plants, like our mitochondria, contain their own DNA.

DNA was discovered by Friedrich Miescher in 1869 ... from the pus in bandages he collected from a hospital. Its role in genetics was not realised until much later.

Watson and Crick announced the double helix design of DNA on 28 February 1953 in The Eagle pub in Cambridge.
(They have good beer there too!)

When replicating, DNA gets tightly wound up as it's unzipped, and needs special enzymes to cut the strands to relieve the strain.

About 8% of our genome comes from old viruses that inserted their DNA into ours!

(Reads from Wikipedia) DNA was the pseudonym taken by the two British dance music producers Nick Batt and Neal Slateford!

Chromosomes are DNA packed tightly around proteins called histones. Chromosomes can only be seen in a dividing cell.

Genetics is the study of heredity. Or why you should look like your mom and dad, not your mom and the milkman.

Dolly the sheep was the first cloned mammal. They named her after Dolly Parton because the DNA used came from a mammary gland.

Green Fluorescent Protein (GFP) in deep-sea jellyfish makes them glow. Geneticists harness the GFP gene to study other organisms.

# Your Favourite Science Acronyms (YFSA␣␣That␣s Not Clever at All)

Science, Technology, Engineering and Mathematics **(STEM)**

Weakly Interacting Massive Particles **(WIMPs)**

Massive Compact Halo Objects **(MACHOs)**

Frequency-Resolved Optical Gating **(FROG)**

Sensitive High-Resolution Ion
MicroProbe **(SHRIMP)**

Grand Unified Theory **(GUT)**

Light Amplification by Stimulated
Emission of Radiation **(LASER)**

Superconducting Quantum
Interference Devices **(SQUIDs)**,
used to detect tiny magnetic fields

Spontaneously Pulsating
Ultradense Stars **(SPUDS)**

Time And Relative Dimension
in Space **(TARDIS)**

Chronic Obstructive Lung
Disease **(COLD)**

# Colourful Science!

The Sun (technically a Yellow Dwarf) would appear white to our eyes if viewed from outside the Earth's atmosphere (don't try it).

Both the sky and the sea appear blue because short wavelength light (blue) is scattered more readily than long wavelength light (red).

A black hole is black because its gravity is so dense that even light can't escape. It's even darker than the back of your shed!

Mauve (mauveine) was the first synthetic dye, discovered serendipitously in 1856 by Sir William Perkin.

Cataracts cause eyes to be less sensitive to blue light, hence old ladies get blue rinses to compensate — it seems white to them.

Many of the genes controlling colour vision are on the X chromosome, making colour blindness more common in men than women.

In human eyes, colour is detected via three types of specialised cone cells (S, M and L), each sensitive to different light wavelengths.

All of the colours you can see are actually a narrow part of the spectrum. Imagine seeing it all!

Using a prism, Sir Isaac Newton split white light into the spectrum of red, orange, yellow, green, cyan, blue and violet light.

# More Frogs ...

Most frogs have teeth in their upper jaw (to hold their prey). Only one species has teeth on its lower jaw (*Gastrotheca guentheri*).

The male Darwin's frog keeps all his mate's surviving eggs in his mouth until they emerge as fully grown froglets! It's called mouth brooding!

*Rana sylvatica* (wood frogs) have natural 'antifreeze' in their cells. They can freeze solid and hop away after thawing out.

Frog bones form a new ring every year when they are hibernating. Just like trees, you can count these rings to find out their age!

The 5-centimetre golden poison dart frog is the most poisonous animal on the planet – producing enough venom to kill 10 humans.

The world's largest frog is the Goliath frog. It grows up to 33 centimetres long and weighs nearly 3 kilograms.
They can jump 3 metres!

Frogs don't turn into princes if you kiss them!

*Huia cavitympanum*, found in Borneo, is the only frog that can communicate using purely ultrasonic calls – up to 38 kilohertz.

# USE THE FORCE ...

A force is what changes or tends to change the motion of an object.

Forces make things go, stop, twist, turn or move. How would you open that bottle of wine without forces? Or open a chocolate bar?

There are four fundamental forces in nature: gravity, electromagnetism, weak nuclear force and strong nuclear force.

Gravity is the force whose charge is mass – it is very weak but there are no negative charges, so it adds up.

Gravity is the weakest of the fundamental forces, but it has infinite range and is the dominant force at large distances.

Gravity causes attraction between all bodies and is proportional to the object's mass. It stops you reaching new heights!

# USE THE FORCE ... CONTD

Electromagnetism is the force between electrically charged bodies – it's the force we experience most often in our daily lives.

The strong nuclear force is the glue that binds quarks and atoms together. Only over tiny areas or all atoms would clump up crazily!

The strong nuclear force gets stronger at larger distances. The three other fundamental forces get weaker at larger distances.

The weak nuclear force is responsible for radioactivity – the Sun would not burn without it!

Centrifugal force is actually not a force at all, but an object being swung round trying to go in a straight line.

# Shocking Facts on Electricity

All animals that attack prey using electric pulses are aquatic. Only in a low-resistance medium is such an approach effective.

In 1791, Luigi Galvani demonstrated that electricity was the means by which nerve cells send signals to muscles.

The Van de Graaf generators often used in school science demonstrations are actually capable of generating a few million volts.

The crackling noise you sometimes hear when taking off a jumper is actually hundreds of lightning bolts caused by a static charge.

Copper, silver and gold are the best conductors because they all have one unpaired S electron in their outer Orbital, taking or giving electrons.

The lightning you see when you pull apart a bandage's packaging in the dark is called triboluminescence.

# More on the Earth

 The Earth is the only planet in the solar system with zebras on it. That's pretty amazing.

 The core of planet Earth is likely to be made from giant magnetised iron crystals.

 Our magnetic field occasionally flips over. We can see this recorded in formed crust under the sea floor.

 The magnetic field directs meteorites towards the poles, also into banana-shaped back-and-forth pathways: Van Allen belts.

Without our magnetic field, high-energy particles and radiation from the Sun would kill us off.

When we see an aurora, we see atoms in our upper atmosphere being struck by particles from the solar wind.

 Earth is the most dense planet in the solar system, Saturn is the least dense.

 Saturn is 95 times the mass of Earth, yet its density is so low that if put in water it would float!

 The oldest dated rocks on Earth are meteorites; many of these are 4.54 billion years old.

 The distance from the Earth to the Sun is 150 million kilometres, and increasing by 15 metres per century.

 Earth formed 4.6 billion years ago, when the solar system coalesced from a huge rotating cloud of gas and dust – the solar nebula.

 Earth's orbit is not a perfect circle, it is an oval-shaped ellipse, just like that of the orbits of all the other planets.

 While there are 365.26 solar days in a year, in the same period the Earth rotates 366.26 times.

# 'We're Going to Need a Bigger Boat!'

# More on SHARKS!

Sharks become immobile when they are flipped upside down — it's called tonic immobility. You could, technically, rub a Great White's belly ;)

Killer whales exploit tonic immobility by flipping sharks on their backs and holding them there until they suffocate.

Some species of shark practise intrauterine cannibalism — pups eat one another in the womb (serious survival of the fittest)!

Contrary to popular belief, sharks do get cancer!

Sharks and rays are cartilaginous fish. This means the structure of the animal's body is formed of cartilage instead of bone.

The fastest shark ever recorded was a Mako (Isurus oxyrinchus). It was clocked swimming at 96 kilometres (60 miles) per hour.

Megalodon was a prehistoric shark (28 to 1.5 million years ago) the size of a bus (16 metres). The largest tooth found was over 8 centimetres long!

# Seriously?

Prawn crackers stick to your tongue because of a bubble-like cell structure. Saliva dissolves the edges of some cells, forming a vacuum.

Earth's air is finite. Yes, you have breathed the same air as Marilyn Monroe, Julius Caesar, Leonardo da Vinci and dinosaurs.

A noble gas is not related to an event that occurs after a monarch eats a curry!

Earth's gravity isn't strong enough to hold helium in the atmosphere. Burst a balloon and any helium inside is lost forever.

Helium was discovered in the Sun in 1868 before it was found on Earth in 1895!

Your body contains enough *phosphorous* to make 2,200 matches!

The bacteria in your gut are *thought to* outnumber the amount of your 'own' cells in your body by about 10 to 1.

Human beings have created 295 exabytes of information. If we *put these onto* CD-ROMs the stack would *stretch beyond the* moon!

The smell of lemon and lime is caused by mirror images (enantiomers) of the exact same molecule – Limonene.

Old books smell nice because lignin in *paper* breaks down over *time to* form vanillin, a fragrant compound used in *perfumes!*

Carbon dating works because living *things* stop taking in carbon when they die. It does not work on rocks.

# MORE ANIMAL FACTS...

Male cuttlefish can disguise themselves as females (to fool rival males) by changing colour via cells known as chromatophores.

The most intelligent invertebrate animal is the octopus — capable of advanced learning, problem-solving, ingenuity and tool use.

Howler monkeys are the world's loudest land animals. The sound is up to 90 decibels, and can be heard from almost 5 kilometres away.

The fat in a camel's hump acts as an insulator from the sun in the day and then keeps the camel warm at night.

A mata-mata turtle engulfs whole fish in roughly 1/15th the time it takes you to blink.

The rock hyrax (looks like a guinea pig) is the closest living 'relative' species to the elephant.

# More
## Science Poems

Darwin spoke of evolution,
And brought with it revolution.
Wallace, too, found the solution,
We must not forget his contribution!

Astronaut Dish and Astronaut Spoon
Jumped in a rocket and flew to the Moon
The dog, cat and cow
Instead launched a rockoon.

Hubble has his constant,
Newton is a force,
Pascal's under pressure,
And Kelvin does heat endorse.

Periodic table?
I sit in first place!
I'm not really stable,
But that's no disgrace …

A koala is a sexy thing,
I'll tell you what the reason is,
Instead of just a single one,
The charmer has two penises.

Don't forget the lady koala,
For nothing could be finer.
Like most marsupials she has two wombs
And a trio of vaginas.

Roses aren't red
Violets aren't blue
They only reflect wavelengths
Of respective hue.

H+O+O again
The combination making rain
Add NaCl it makes the sea
Feeds all plants with Ca and K
Makes up 75% of me.

Twinkle, twinkle, little star
I don't wonder what you are
For by spectroscopic ken
I know that you are hydrogen.

When you find your cat has peed
Soda water's what you need
It will neutralise the smell
Which we know is pongy hell.

# More Bright Sparks

## Famous Scientists!

Irish scientist John Tyndall is a founding
father of modern climate science and
the man who first explained why the
sky is blue!

Francis Beaufort (1774–1857):
Creator of the Beaufort scale which is
used to describe the force and
velocity of wind.

Rosalind Franklin collected X-ray diffraction
data that helped Watson and Crick unravel
the structure of DNA.

Ernst Haeckel (1834–1919):
German polymath, who advocated Darwinism and coined the terms ecology, phylum, phylogeny, stem cell and Protista.

Lord Kelvin (1824–1907):
Irish scientist, who introduced the Kelvin scale. His work led to the second Law of Thermodynamics.

Lóránd Eötvös constructed his double-beam torsion balance 110 years ago. The oldest university in Hungary is named after him.

Gregor Mendel (1822–1884):
An Augustinian friar who demonstrated the underlying principles of heredity and laid the groundwork for modern genetics using pea plants.

Dmitri Mendeleev (1834–1907) was a Russian chemist who created the Periodic Table. He also created the standard for vodka production of 40% alcohol.

Rene Laennec (1781–1826) invented the stethoscope in 1816 which was later used to diagnose his own tuberculosis.

Cecilia Payne-Gaposchkin (1900–1979) discovered as a PhD student that the Sun was mostly hydrogen, not iron.

Lise Meitner (1878–1968) was the first woman to get a PhD in physics. She worked on a mobile X-ray unit for the First World War and was the co-discoverer of fission.

# Polar Bears are Cool (Well, Sometimes They're Cold)

Polar bears are only naturally found in the Arctic region while penguins are only naturally found in the Antarctic region.

Polar bears are not actually all left-handed. This is an Inuit myth that somehow became an 'interesting fact'.

Polar bears appear white, but their fur is transparent and their skin is black!

Polar bears first appeared 5 million years ago.

# You Know What Gets on my Nerves?

# Myelin

There are only 10 types of people
in the world: *those who understand binary
and those who don't.*

•••

The Heineken Uncertainty Principle says:
'You can never be sure how many beers
you had last night.'

•••

We had a binary relationship ...
She turned me on, I turned her off.

•••

What's the difference between
cooking and chemistry?
In chemistry you can't lick the spoon.

Calvin to Krebs,
'I challenge you to a bike race.'

•••

A successful aircraft landing is a
controlled midair collision with a planet.

•••

Schrödinger's cat has surgery.
Nervously, Erwin asks the doc how it went.
'Well,' says the doctor,
'I've got good news and bad news.'

•••

Optimist: Glass is half full.
Pessimist: Glass half empty.
Engineer: Glass twice as big as
it needs to be.

•••

I know a couple of jokes about
microwave photons.
They aren't very exciting.

# LET'S GET SERIOUS ABOUT SOME PHYSICS FOR A MINUTE!

Noise-cancelling headphones create sound waves of the same amp and frequency, but 180 degrees out of phase with noise. Cancel out = destructive interference.

Celestial mechanics is the study of the motions and gravitational interactions of stellar and planetary systems.

A scalar quantity has magnitude only. Famous scalar quantities include speed, distance, mass, charge and all forms of energy.

A vector quantity has both magnitude and direction. Famous vector quantities include velocity, acceleration, force and momentum.

Acceleration is defined as the rate of change of velocity. It is a vector quantity and is measured in metres per second squared.

Newton's first law: An object will continue to move at a constant velocity unless acted upon by a resultant force.

Newton's second law: Force is directly proportional to the rate of change of momentum (or to put it more usefully, F = ma).

Newton's third law: If object A exerts a force on object B, object B will exert an equal and opposite force on object A.

Physics is the eternal search for an application for carbon nanotubes.

The universe has a built-in speed limit, the speed of light in a vacuum c = 299,792,458 metres per second. Nothing can go faster than this!

There are only four theories of physics: Newtonian Mechanics, Thermodynamics (heat), Quantum Mechanics and General Relativity (gravity).

'Physicist' was coined in 1840 by the Rev. William Whewell to denote a 'cultivator of physics' as opposed to a physician.

A compass points at our magnetic, not geographic, poles. If you take it to the North Pole, it will try to point downwards!

Watt invented the steam engine. Watt is a unit of power. These sentences can cause confusion in physics oral exams.

# Know any Jokes About Sodium? Na!

Wanna hear a joke about nitric oxide?
NO.

Why did the chicken cross the road?
Newton: 'Chickens at rest tend to stay at rest
and chickens in motion tend to cross roads.'

Two geologists walking along an outcrop.
One says, 'This rock is not metamorphised.'
The other replies, 'No schist!'

Two antennae met, fell in love and got married.
The ceremony was OK but the reception
was brilliant.

# Time

'The only reason for time is so that everything doesn't happen at once.' Albert Einstein

The speed of light is constant to all observers (no matter how fast they are travelling). Hence, time is relative.

Time travels slower the closer you are to a gravity well, so your feet are slightly younger than your eyebrows.

Too close to a black hole, both time and space warp. The black hole becomes inescapable because it now exists in your future.

Distance units are defined by time and constant light speed. A metre is the distance light travels in 1/299792458 of a second.

Planck time:
0.0000000000000000000000000000000000000000000043
seconds. Nothing can happen over a shorter time than
this.

It takes 8 minutes 22 seconds for the light from the Sun
to reach Earth.

Looking at stars and galaxies, we in fact see them as
they were billions of years ago.

When drawing graphs, time generally goes on the x-axis
since it is an independent variable!

Even a stopped clock tells the right time twice a day.

# Subatomic Particles – the Stuff Atoms are Made of

There are 6 types of quarks, known as flavours: up, down, strange, charm, bottom and top.

Leptons are a group of fundamental particles. They include the electron, muon and tau particle along with their matching neutrinos.

Electrons orbit the nucleus at distinct distances, light is emitted when an electron changes orbit to one closer to the nucleus.

A muon is a particle which decays after 3.5 millionths of a second. If they travel fast enough, they appear to live for minutes.

Baryons are made of three quarks and include protons, neutrons, their antiparticles and the lamda and the sigma particle.

Mesons are hadrons made of two quarks consisting of a quark and an antiquark. Examples include pions, kaons and eta mesons.

If you try to separate two quarks it takes up enough energy to make two new quarks. $E = mc^2$.

# Chemistry can be interesting too ...

A battery is a contained chemical reaction. Electrons move from one compound to another and in the process power your device.

The molecule buckminsterfullerene or C60 is known as 'buckyballs' because of the unique shape formed by its 60 carbon atoms.

Combining four elements (C, H, O and N) can make more compounds than combining all of the other elements left in the periodic table. The largest known protein, titin, has an IUPAC name that stretches to 189,819 letters!

The guy who invented aspirin (acetylation of salicylic acid) invented heroin (acetylation of morphine) by the same process.

Humphrey Davy, who isolated at least six elements for the first time, was found with 200 times the natural level of mercury in his hair.

An acid is a proton donor, a base is a proton acceptor.

# SCIENCE
# OUTSIDE THE LAB

Vegetable oil and magnetic ink/toner for a printer make a great ferrofluid – all you need to do is add a magnet.

Get an empty drinks can and a balloon. Rub the balloon on your hair. Hold balloon near can. Watch it roll.

Draw round your shadow each hour to make yourself into a sundial. Where your shadow is shortest is solar noon.

Red cabbage water as a natural indicator – add vinegar, it goes red; add bicarbonate of soda, it goes green.

Dissolve as much sugar as you can into boiling water, then pour into a jar. Hang a string into the water. Leave and watch crystals grow!

Rinse a plastic bottle with diluted alcohol. Use a bike pump to increase pressure inside. Release quickly and make a cloud in a bottle!

Clean silver with water, bicarbonate and foil. The bicarb removes oxide on the foil, the foil reacts with the tarnish.

# Entropy isn't what it used to be

WANTED: Schrödinger's Cat. Dead and/or alive.

The most literate dinosaur was the Thesaurus.

Molecular biologists always have the latest fashion. They all have designer genes.

If you aren't part of the solution, you're part of the precipitate.

We mustn't look at quantum computers when they perform an operation otherwise they'll pretend to be as silly as regular ones.

A travelling electron saw some particle physicists watching it, so it turned to wave.

I've looked into invisibility physics and, personally, I just can't see it.

What did the mathematician say when he'd had too much food? $\sqrt{(-1/64)}$

What do you get if you cross an octopus with a cow? A rebuke from the ethics committee, and your funding stopped.

What do you get if you cross a mountaineer with a mosquito? Nothing: You can't cross a scalar with a vector.

What is the coefficient of friction of a cat? Mu.

Necrophilia in animals is called Davian behaviour. As someone called Dave, I consider this a slanderous outrage.

Mrs Schrödinger to Mr Schrödinger: 'What the hell did you do to the cat?'

Heisenberg was driving too fast and got pulled over. Cop: 'Do you know how fast you were going?' Heisenberg: 'No, but I know where I am.'

# More Random Stuff!

Florence Nightingale wasn't the greatest nurse, but was an excellent statistician. She popularised the use of the pie chart!

If you see a double rainbow, the colours in the second, fainter one are upside-down.

One of the largest living things is the honey fungus mushroom in Malheur National Forest, in Oregon, USA. It covers 2,200 acres (mostly underground).

Among other things, alcohol suppresses ADH release, inhibiting $H_2O$ reabsorption in the kidneys. That's why you pee more when drunk!

People who have ever lived: 70 billion.
People alive: 7 billion.
Therefore 10% of people are immortal.

# *The* Marvellous Human Body

The average length of the small intestine is about 7 metres.

Humans have four nostrils – two external and two internal.

The internal nostrils are called choana and connect the nose to the throat.

Your blood is derived from bone, which means it is technically a connective tissue.

On average a human cell interacts with $10^8$ different antigens, requiring the cell to have the same number of antibodies.

Human thigh bones are stronger than concrete.

Your brain uses 20% of the oxygen that enters your bloodstream.

90% of the cells in your body are not human! They are organisms such as bacteria and fungi.

Each square inch (4 square centimetres) of human skin contains 20 feet (6 metres) of blood vessels.

Every person has a unique tongue print.

There are nearly 650 skeletal muscles in the human body.

Adult lungs have a surface area of around 70 square metres.

Humans shed about 600,000 particles of skin every hour – 0.8 kilograms a year. That's 50 kilograms of skin by the age of 70.

By the time you turn 70, your heart will have beaten two-and-a-half billion times (assuming an average of 70 beats per minute).

A fingernail or toenail takes about 6 months to grow from base to tip.

A human being loses an average of 40 to 100 strands of hair a day.

# Spiders and Insects

Water striders hunt on the water supported by surface tension. As they grow, their limbs grow disproportionately longer.

The smallest aerial insects don't really fly using lift – they paddle through the air.

The largest flying insects in Earth's history were probably the meganeurid dragonflies, which had wingspans just over 60 centimetres.

Lundy cabbage flea beetles live on a 2.5 kilometre strip, 27.5 metres wide on the island of Lundy in the Bristol Channel – and nowhere else.

*Phobaeticus chani*, a type of Phasmid (stick insect) is the world's longest insect. The body can measure up to 35.8 centimetres.

Army ants do not construct nests. They live together in a 'bivouac', a nest made up of hundreds of thousands of living ant bodies.

Locusts can eat their own weight in food in a day. A person eats his own body weight in about half a year.

Houseflies can taste with their feet. Their receptors are allegedly 10 million times more sensitive to sugar than the human tongue.

The house fly 'hums' in the key of F.

Ants 3 millimetres long have been observed dragging prey 6 millimetres long back to nest – the equivalent of us dragging a car by our teeth over a distance of 8 kilometres!

# Health

Diabetes mellitus and Diabetes insipidus were named after how the sufferers' urine tasted — mellitus = sweet; insipidus = flavourless.

Your immune system actually rewrites your DNA to make new antibodies.

The smallpox vaccine was the first successful vaccine. It was discovered by E. Jenner in 1796 with the help of some milkmaids.

# More

# Wise Words from the Masters

'Observations buried
in a desk are no observations.'
*F. W. A. Argelander*, encouraging amateur
astronomy (Prussia, 1844)

'If I could remember the names of all those
particles, I'd be a botanist.'
*Enrico Fermi*, one of the founders of
quantum mechanics

'Nothing in life is to be feared,
it is only to be understood.'
*Marie Curie*

'Genius is 1% inspiration and
99% perspiration.'
*Thomas A. Edison*

'Philosophy of science is as useful to
scientists as ornithology is to birds.'
*Richard Feynman*

'You are not thinking,
you are just being logical.'
*Niels Bohr*

'Knowledge is the food of the soul.'
*Plato*

'Inventas vitam juvat excoluisse per artes.'
('And they who bettered life on Earth
by new-found mastery.')
Inscription on the Nobel Prize

'Science … never solves a problem
without creating ten more.'
*George Bernard Shaw*

'In science, the credit goes to the man who
convinces the world, not the man to whom
the idea first occurs.'
*Sir Francis Darwin*

'All science is either physics or
stamp collecting.'
*Ernest Rutherford*

# Radioactive Cats Have 18 Half-Lives

Einstein, on a train, to the conductor: 'Excuse me, what time does Cambridge stop at this train?'

Did you hear about the biologist who had twins? She baptised one and kept the other as a control.

Two chemists walk into a bar.
First guy: 'I'll have some $H_2O$.'
Second guy: 'I'll have some $H_2O$ too.'
Second guy dies.

There are two types of people in the world. Those who know how to extrapolate from incomplete data ...

Resistance is futile if <1 ohm.

On a holiday flight, 22 said to 7, 'Let's not be divided on this.' 'No way!' says 22. 'After all, it'd just be pi in the sky.'

# The Science of Sex

Sexual reproduction is when two cells, each with half of the DNA needed, combine and create a living cell.

Asexual reproduction: no gene mixing so all offspring are identical copies of the parent, e.g. greenfly and strawberry plants.

Certain species of lizards have only females. During breeding season, one female mimics a male.

Human orgasms, in both sexes, have contractions of reproductive structures, occurring at about 0.8-second intervals.

Genes for the red and green photoreceptors are on the X chromosome. Polymorphisms enable women to see more colours than men.

Ewes' ovulation only occurs during the autumn. Thus, most lambs are born in spring, when their chances of survival are optimal.

There can be as many as 350 million sperm cells per ejaculation! Most are killed instantly in the vagina by acidic mucus.

The sex organ on a male spider is located at the end of one of its legs.

A female hyena is equipped with a pseudo-penis, which is basically an enlarged clitoris, they can erect it at will.

Most mammal males have a baculum ('penis bone'). Exceptions include horses, spider monkeys and humans.

The largest cell in the human body is the female egg and the smallest is the male sperm.

Seahorses and other pipefish are unique in that gametes flow from the female to the male and the males get pregnant.

Male pregnancy in seahorses leads to females showing 'male-typical' behaviours of increased promiscuity.

For body size, humans have the longest penis of all primates. Gorillas have the smallest (approximately 2 centimetres when erect). Chimps have the largest testes.

The word 'orchid', now used most often to refer to plants, comes from a Greek word meaning 'testicle'.

Ribbon eels all change sex (and colour) as they mature. All individuals are born male.

Platypus XY sex chromosomes travel in chains of five. One end reptilian/avian, other mammalian. Suggests one evolved from the other.

If a tortoiseshell cat is male, it's because it has an XXY genotype. Male cats are usually one colour.

Sacculina is a parasitic barnacle that castrates crabs and makes them tend Sacculina eggs as if they were the crab's own.

Social sex determination! In the harems of the fish *Halichoeres melanurus*, if the male dies, the biggest female will become male.

Female koalas have 3 vaginas, making them 33.3% sexier than male koalas who have bifurcated penises.

In humans, gender is determined by X and Y chromosomes: XX = female; XY = male.

In birds, gender is determined by Z and W chromosomes: ZW = female; ZZ = male.

In grasshoppers, gender is determined by the number of X chromosomes: XX = female; X = male.

In embryos, there is a signalling molecule that is crucial for correct development. It is called Sonic Hedgehog! Seriously!

# SCIENCE

# AT HOME

The refrigerator works on the premise that heat will always flow from a hot body to a cooler one ... that's why back of fridge is hot!

I've got sodium-free salt in my kitchen. As salt is NaCl, that means sodium-free salt is just Cl – chlorine. It's bleach, essentially. Ruins chips.

Once the adult housefly hatches from the pupal stage, it has an approximate life span of 15 to 30 days.

House flies can travel up to 9.6 kilometres in 24 hours.

Ironing works by using heat and weight to stretch polymer molecules, removing creases. This doesn't make it less dull as a chore.

Baking powder works because sodium hydrogen carbonate releases $CO_2$ when it is heated in an oven.

Old-style TVs used a cathode ray tube, containing an electron gun and a phosphor-coated screen that fluoresced.

Modern flat-screen TVs use either plasma (the fourth state of matter), LCDs, LEDs or OLEDs.

Natural gas (piped to your oven/hob/boiler) is mainly methane ($CH_4$). It's normally odourless but has a smell added for safety.

Before the invention of the lightbulb, it was next to impossible to look like you were having an idea.

Detergents contain surfactants with hydrophobic and hydrophilic ends, which reduce surface tension and allow things to get wet.

There's no difference in water rotation direction in toilets between the northern and southern hemispheres.

Adding salt to water raises its boiling point — but at a palatable concentration, not enough that you'd notice.

Shower curtains stick to you because water droplets create an area of low pressure next to you.

# You're such a plank — quantum physics

'I think I can safely say that nobody understands quantum mechanics.' *Richard Feynman*

Quantum mechanics – describing a tiny world using truly massive words. It's about quirky things called quarks.

Quantum mechanics describes how energy and matter interact and behave at the extreme.

A quantum is the minimum amount of a physical entity in an interaction, e.g. photon = light quantum;
Baby Bel = cheese quantum.

We can never know exactly what a particle at the quantum scale is doing. Looking at it needs light, which affects its behaviour.

I took my car to a quantum mechanic. When I went to pick it up, he couldn't tell me where it was but he knew how fast it was going.

A particle small enough is also a wave, spread out in space – photons, electrons, neutrons, that sort of thing.

The quantum world is just a bit weird and no one really understands it.

'Quantum' has replaced 'atomic' as the term scientists use most often to confuse/intimidate non-scientists.

But it don't mean a thing if it ain't got that string!

You can only know the former state of a quantum particle, the present state is unknowable as observation alters it.

# Even More Bright Sparks

William Thomson, First Baron Kelvin, gave us the first and second laws of thermodynamics, absolute zero and the Kelvin temperature scale.

Michael Faraday, physicist and chemist. Worked on electromagnetism, discovered magnetic field, benzene. Created first electric motor.

James C. Maxwell developed Faraday's work into electromagnetism equations, which was the basis for Einstein's work. Created the first colour photo.

Obstetric forceps were invented by the Chamberlen family. They kept them secret for 150 years by blindfolding everyone at the birth.

Hugh (the elder) Chamberlen tried to sell the forceps idea in 1670 but a demonstration killed the mother and baby. Worst *Dragons' Den* ever.

Sir Frank Whittle (1907–1996) patented and developed the world's first turbojet engine. I bet his neighbours loved him.

Francis Crick (1916–2004) was a co-discoverer of the structure of DNA in 1953 with James D. Watson.

Craig Venter (b. 1946) played a role in sequencing the human genome and in creating the first cell with a synthetic genome.

Eric Kandel discovered the mechanism of the synapse using a giant slug, warranting a rare gastropod-inspired Nobel Prize.

Jane Goodall, celebrated primatologist, observed chimps who used tools.

J.J. Thomson (1856–1940) discovered the electron in 1897 and determined its mass/charge ratio. He was awarded the Nobel Prize in 1906.

Louis de Broglie, a French physicist, introduced the idea of 'electron waves' and the wave-particle duality theory of matter in 1924.

Erwin Schrödinger, an Austrian Nazi-hating, lady-loving physicist. Pioneer of quantum physics and creator of Schrödinger's cat thought experiment.

Charles Darwin ate a rare bird specimen that he had been searching for in vain – then the poor creature was named after him!

Barbara McClintock won the 1983 Nobel Prize (Medicine and Physiology) for her revolutionary work in genetic theory and gene functioning.

Isaac Newton once stared at the Sun until he went temporarily blind, and spent the next two weeks in a dark room recovering.

# Sexy Numbers

Sexy prime: Two prime numbers that differ from each other by six – e.g. 5 and 11.

Sexy prime triplets: Triplets of primes that are also sexy primes – e.g. 7, 13 and 19.

Sexy quadruplets: Four primes that are also sexy – e.g. 11, 17, 23 and 29.

Sexy quintuplets. Five primes that are also sexy. There is only one example of sexy quintuplets, 5, 11, 17, 23 and 29.

# Happy Numbers

Happy number: Any positive integer that when you replace it by the sum of the squares of its digits and repeat this, you get 1.

Happy primes: A number that is both happy and prime.

Unhappy number (or sad number): Any number that when you follow the process for happy numbers does not result in 1.

# Magic Maths

$19 = (1 \times 9 + 1 + 9)$ and $29 = (2 \times 9 + 2 + 9)$.
This also works for 39, 49, 59, 69, 79, 89 and 99.

To multiply 10,112,359,550,561,797,752,808,988,76
4,044,943,820,224,719 by 9, move the 9 at the end to
the front.

73 is the 21st prime. Its mirror, 37, is the 12th prime.

$7 \times 3 = 21$. The square root of 73 is 8.544. $8 + 5 + 4 + 4 = 21$.

If you multiply $1,089 \times 9$ you get 9,801.

$10 \times 9 \times 8 \times 7 \times 6 \times 5 \times 4 \times 3 \times 2 \times 1$ seconds is exactly
six weeks!

60 is the smallest number that can be divided by
1, 2, 3, 4, 5 and 6. This is why the Babylonians used
it to count time.

$111,111,111 \times 111,111,111 = 12,345,678,987,654,321$

# Cool Numbers

−273.15°C is 0°K (Kelvin), or absolute zero. A very cool number indeed.

Favourite ratio: 16:9 – could watch it all day.

The speed of light is roughly a foot per nanosecond. The speed of sound is roughly a foot per millisecond.

Count to 60 on your hands by multiplying segments of fingers on one hand by the fingers of the other hand.

Fibonacci sequence: 0, 1, 1, 2, 3, 5, 8, etc. – each number is the sum of the previous two. It appears in nature (and *The da Vinci Code*).

A parsec is equal to roughly 30 trillion kilometres. An attoparsec (quintillionth of a parsec) which is about 3.085 centimetres.

10,000,000,000,000,000,000 = 10 quintillion (1 with 19 zeros), the number of transistors that Intel ships in a year!

1995 was the seventh year of the Japanese emperor's reign: 17 runners ran 7,777 metres round the Imperial Palace at 7 minutes past 7 on 7/7.

Louis XIV ascended to the throne in 1643 (1 + 6 + 4 + 3 = 14) and reigned for 77 years (7 + 7 = 14) and died in 1715 (1 + 7 + 1 + 5 = 14).

A Googol is 1 followed by 100 zeros. 1 followed by googol zeros is a googolplex. Google's headquaters is the googleplex.

Never ask a mathematician to recite the digits of Pi ($\pi$), you'll never hear the end of it.

Fear of the number 666 is called hexakosioihexekontahexaphobia. This, in turn, is scary to people with a phobia of long words.

The number most commonly displayed on calculators is 58,008.

The sum of the divisors of 28 is 28 (1 + 2 + 4 + 7 + 14), so it's a perfect number! The smallest perfect number is 6 (1 + 2 + 3).

# EVEN MORE
## Science Poems

If you're doing as you oughter,
Add the acid to the water;
May your rest be long and placid
If you add the water to the acid.

When turning a corner,
In a high-speed car,
Don't forget that force,
Is mv2 over r!

The greatest dance of all,
To which the universe will bend,
Is the dance between 4 forces
And 12 particle elements.

There was a scientist called Newton.
Had a theory, a beaut one.
An apple fell. He let out a yell.
And got a box to put fruit in.

A wonderful thing is a mother,
A wonderful thing I say.
To aid your synthetics,
Gave half her genetics
And all of your mDNA.

153

# The Senses

There are many more than
5 human senses. We can
sense acceleration, pain,
temperature, carbon dioxide
and more.

'Anosmia' is the term for
loss of the sense of smell.
The most frequent cause
is the common cold.

Astronauts lose their sense of smell in space, so they can't taste food properly – no one really knows why.

'Synaesthesia' is a neurological condition in which one sense is experienced as another – e.g. sound perceived as visual sensation.

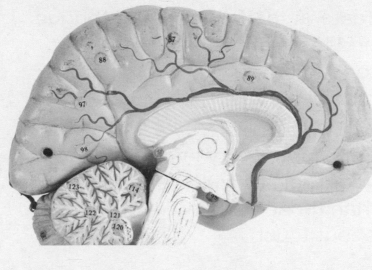

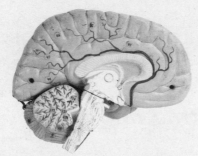

Human retinas are back to front, the capillaries and nerves are in front of the photoreceptors. Our eyes adapt to filter them out.

Taste at the front of your tongue and taste at the back of your tongue are run by two different cranial nerves.

Pain fibres carry information to your brain at a slower speed than those carrying information about touch.

Allodynia is when a stimulus that is not normally painful (e.g. light or touch) is felt as pain.

Proprioception (the forgotten sense!) is the sense of relative position and rate of movement of different parts of the body.

Cats have a layer in their eyes (tapetum lucidum) that reflects light back, allowing better vision in low light.

# Earthquakes

Seismology is the study of earthquakes and seismic waves that move through and around the Earth.

It's estimated that several million earthquakes occur each year. Many are missed as they hit remote areas or have tiny magnitudes.

The largest earthquake ever recorded was a magnitude 9.5 in Chile on 22 May 1960.

The deadliest earthquake ever struck on 23 January 1556 in Shansi, China. Some 830,000 people are estimated to have died.

# SLIPPERY SCIENCE—
## OIL

The first oil producers were the Chinese, in 327. There oil was called burning water and was used for salt production.

Rudolf Diesel originally invented the internal combustion engine to run on peanut oil.

The word 'petroleum' comes from the Greek *petra* (rock) and the Latin *oleum* (oil).

The United States is the world's largest consumer of petroleum. It is also the third largest producer, but not a major exporter.

Most coal dates from a time between when plants invented 'lignin' and fungi learned to digest it. Now, wood biodegrades, so no more coal!

Olive oil is high in healthy monounsaturated fats. It's also the name of Popeye's girlfriend spelled incorrectly.

Oil doesn't mix with water because water is polar – the oxygen is greedy for electrons – while the carbons and hydrogens share.

In some tropical countries, coconut oil is used in fuel for transport and generators. It has also been tested as engine oil.

Most whale oil was derived from blubber, but sperm whale oil was taken from an organ that sits above the sperm whale skull.

The liver of a shark produces a huge amount of oil to make it more buoyant. Even so, sharks are slightly denser than sea water.

There are bacteria living on your skin and eating the oils it produces.

# WOW!

Every iron atom in your blood was created in the core of a star. The atoms in your two hands probably came from different stars.

Candle flames create around 1.5 million diamond nanoparticles every second they are burning.

A blue whale heart is roughly the size of a compact car.

The oceans contain enough salt to cover all the continents to a depth of nearly 500 feet (152.4 metres)!

A magnetar is the most extreme magnet in the universe, 10,000,000,000,000 times as strong as the Earth's magnetic field.

The brain cannot feel any pain. Amazing!

The Earth does move for you - at 107,300 kilometres per hour round the Sun.

If you were to lay out all the blood vessels in a human body end to end, they would extend 99,779 kilometres (enough to circle the Earth 2.5 times!)

But if you were to lay out all the blood vessels in a human body end to end, you'd probably be arrested!

All breasts are sweat glands modified by evolution. Nobody tell 'FHM'.

# Be Afraid, Be Very Afraid!

A phobia is an intense, irrational fear of something that holds little or no real danger! Tell that to the sharks I'm scared of!

When you are startled, the body produces adrenalin, your own superpower hormone!

Humans and monkeys seem primed to acquire fear of spiders and snakes, but only if they see others afraid first. Social referencing.

Handy phobia for elephants: Suriphobia — a fear of mice!

Handy phobia for mice: Ophidiophobia — a fear of snakes!

162

Handy *phobia* for snakes: Pachydermophobia — a fear of elephants (watch out for *those* big feet!).

## WORST PHOBIAS FOR TEACHERS!

Scolionophobia — Fear of school

Ephebiphobia — Fear of teenagers

Glossophobia — Fear of public speaking

## PHOBIAS FOR VAMPIRES!

Alliumphobia — Fear of garlic

Staurophobia — Fear of crucifixes

Phengophobia — Fear of daylight!

## MORE RANDOM, WEIRD PHOBIAS

Alekorphobia — Fear of chickens

Allodoxaphobia — Fear of opinions

Anablephobia — Fear of looking *up*

Aulophobia — Fear of flutes

Barophobia — Fear of gravity

Bibliophobia — Fear of books

Botanophobia — Fear of *plants*

Cacophobia — Fear of ugliness

Catoptrophobia — Fear of mirrors

Chronomentrophobia – Fear of clocks

Coulrophobia – Fear of clowns

Domatophobia – Fear of houses

Friggatriskaidekaphobia – Fear of Friday the 13th

Gamophobia – Fear of marriage

Genuphobia – Fear of knees

Heliophobia – Fear of the Sun

Hippopotomonstrosesquippedaliophobia – Fear of long words (that's just cruel)

Koumpounophobia – Fear of buttons

Lalophobia – Fear of speaking

Mageirocophobia – Fear of cooking

Medomalacuphobia – Fear of losing an erection

Papaphobia – Fear of the Pope

Peladophobia – Fear of bald people

Pentheraphobia – Fear of your mother-in-law

Ponophobia – Fear of overworking

Somniphobia – Fear of sleep

Venustraphobia – Fear of beautiful women!

# Planes, Trains and Automobiles!

A Formula 1 car typically has 80,000 components. So if it was assembled 99.9% correctly, it would start the race with 80 things wrong!

You get a bigger radiation dose on an international flight than wandering around a nuclear plant. Neither causes super powers.

Due to a lack of flat roads, the Model T Ford was also designed to work as a tractor. One was even made into a mobile church.

You can't take thermometers onto a plane because the mercury in them will react with the aluminium the plane's made from.

Aeroplanes go in curved lines, not straight, to reach their destinations, because of geodeisics – it's shorter over a sphere.

An aeroplane's 'black box' is a device that records conditions and events in flight. It's actually orange in colour. Weird!

Even in a full emergency, it can take a train 1.5 kilometres or more to stop (so if the driver can see you, it's already too late to stop!)

If you added it up, Boeing 747s have travelled 56 billion kilometres since the plane was first launched. That's 75,000 times to the moon and back.

# ANCIENT SCIENCE

The Babylonians' number system had base 60 (instead of decimal base 10), hence clocks and degrees are in factors and multiples of 60!

The word 'atom' comes from the Greek word *atomos*, which means uncuttable.

In ancient times, trepanning (drilling a hole in the skull) was a cure for headaches. However counter-intuitive, it sometimes worked.

Surprisingly, the Romans did not have zero in their numbering system!

Aristotle theorised the brain was a secondary organ, used to 'cool the blood'. Some seem to use it just for this in modern times.

Aristotle also thought science could be divided into practical (ethics), theoretical (maths) and poetical (study of poetry!).

Hippocrates' writings also contain the first references to proctoscopy for rectal examination.
Boldly going, etc. etc.

Romans believed health was due to four 'humours' of the body – blood, phlegm, yellow bile and black bile. Hence the phrase 'in good humour'.

Galileo's original telescope had about the same power and much worse optical quality than a pair of today's binoculars.

The Aztecs developed an agriculture system based on man-made floating islands called *chinampas*.

The Chinese invented gunpowder and used it in fireworks. The Arabs worked out how to purify it with potassium nitrate for use in war!

The Olmec may have been the first civilisation in the western hemisphere to develop a writing system.

# MORE ON QUANTUM PHYSICS

Einstein used Planck's new constant to explain the Photo Electric Effect, relating a photon's frequency to an electron's momentum.

Max Planck, trying to experiment with blackbody radiation, discovered energy is quantised by the same amount in every material, $E=hf$.

Planck length: the smallest length in the universe, this means that the universe is pixelated!!

The shortest pixel is the Planck length 0.000 00000000000000000000000000016161 99 metres!

'Quantum tunnelling' means that particles can 'tunnel' into atoms, causing nuclear reactions giving off energy. This happens in stars.

Quantum tunnelling in class: I dare you to run at that wall and see if you go through it.

Without quantum tunnelling, fewer hot stars like the Sun would not be able to shine!

We humans, like quantum particles, are both particles and waves. But as we're huge particles our wavelength is negligible, approximately $10^{-34}$ metres.

Quantum reflection: A ball rolls to the edge of a table and bounces back when it should have fallen off. Happens on a small scale!

# You can't be serious?

Fleas can jump more than
100 times their own height.

You are tallest in the morning because spinal
height increases while sleeping due to fluid flow
into the inter-vertebral discs.

The upturned ends on a commercial aeroplane wing reduce drag at the wingtips. That saves fuel.

Every time an aeroplane takes off, it leaves a vortex on the runway that takes time to vanish. That's why they space out takeoffs.

Sunsets are red because all the bounced blue light is all used up far away over the horizon – you see what's left, the red.

330 million years ago Earth's atmosphere had 1.6 times the oxygen it has today – enabling insects to grow to giant sizes!

Most species of life on Earth are parasitic. Nasty.

The crack of a whip is a sonic boom. The tip travels faster than the speed of sound. The whip was the first man-made object to break the sound barrier.

The mantis shrimp has the most advanced eyesight in the world. It can see in ultraviolet, visible and infrared light.

The most intelligent invertebrate animal is the octopus, which is capable of advanced learning, problem solving, ingenuity and tool use.

Pluto has approximately the same surface area as Russia.

Over 98% of documented species are now extinct.

Despite popular myth, it is never too cold to snow.

The honey badger is the world's most aggressive mammal. They will fight and kill lions, tigers, tortoises, bears and crocodiles.

The matter that comprises the human race could fit into a sugar cube because atoms are 99.999999999% empty space.

In crocodiles, alligators and most turtles, sex is determined by the temperature at which the eggs incubate.

Mercury was used in the making of hats in England. As mercury is toxic, the hat makers would go 'mad', thus the saying 'as mad as a hatter'.

Transistors can switch on and off 300 billion times per second; it would take a human 4,000 years to flick a switch that many times.

# Back to the marvellous
# human body

Every year, your heart beats around 37 million times.

Your stomach lining replaces itself every 3 days, your skin every month and your skeleton every 10 years!

An average 20-year-old human brain contains roughly 150,000 kilometres of nerve cells. That's enough to circle the Earth nearly 4 times.

There are 206 bones in an adult human body and more than 300 in children.

Skin is part of the integumentary system. It can be painted, pierced, cut, sewn, pushed, pulled, tattooed, tanned, covered and exposed.

One human hair can support 100 grams and can stretch by 1.5 times its length before snapping because of its cross-linked structure of keratin.

Normal human cells only divide about 50 times before they die.

An irregular tetrahedron goes into a bar. Barman says, 'You're a diamond geezer, but why the long face?'

Question: What's a tachyon? Answer: A gluon that isn't dry yet.

Two goldfish in a tank. One turns to the other and says, 'Can you drive this thing?'

A Higgs Boson hears organ music coming from a church. It bursts in and shouts, 'STOP! You can't give mass without me!'

What is a bee's favourite dinner?
Spaghetti pollenase.

Did you hear about the guy who broke the law of gravity? He got a suspended sentence.

# Random stuff we couldn't find a title for!

The guy who invented the wheel may have been clever; but the bloke that added the other 3 wheels, now he was a genius ...

Looking at stars and galaxies we in fact see them as they were billions of years ago – so can they see 4.5-billion-year-old Earth?

**Reactions of the alkali metals (Group 1) with water:**

Lithium: pfft

Sodium: Pizzaz

Potassium: Grrrrrr

Rubidium: ROAR!

Caesium: BANG!

Francium: BOOOOM!

(theoretically)

For all the rules and laws science obeys, the English spelling rule of 'i' before 'e' except after 'c' is not one of them!

Estimates for minimum safe distance from a supernova vary … typical estimates are around 100–200 light years.

Do you know why the sperm duct is called the vas deferens?
Well, if you cut it, it makes a vast difference!

Earth's rotation is influenced by the Moon's attraction.
Therefore, every day lasts
0.00000002 seconds
longer than the one
before!

As far as
we know,
Earth is the
only planet to
have just one moon.

Capsaicin is what makes chilli hot, and it's oil soluble. To clean spice off your fingers after cooking, rinse with milk or oil.

Radium was once used in self-luminous paints for watches and clocks, until the painters started to get bone cancer. Whoops!

# What is cystic fibrosis?

Mutations in the CFTR gene can result in organs producing a sticky mucus that obstructs the airways, causing the symptoms of cystic fibrosis.

Cystic fibrosis can affect the lungs, digestive tract, gall bladder, colon, intestines, sinuses, pancreas, liver, sperm ducts, sweat glands and bones!

In 1938, Dorothy Hansine Andersen
(an American physician) was the first person
to describe cystic fibrosis.

Cystic fibrosis is caused by a recessive gene.
You only exhibit the disease if you inherit a faulty
gene from both of your parents.

Ireland has the highest prevalence of cystic
fibrosis in the world with approx 1 in 19 people
carrying a CF mutation.

Around 1 in 25 people of European descent
is a carrier of one allele for cystic fibrosis.

# The Alternative 'A Neutron Walks Into a Bar' Periodic Table

**Nothing (Ng): Naturally occurring element, often found in bank accounts and wallets.**

1. Hydrogen (H): Colourless non-metal gas. The lightest element and it's the most abundant chemical substance. Used as a coolant.

2. Helium (He): Colourless, odourless, non-toxic noble gas. Can't be synthesised in nature. Used in MRI scanners and arc welding.

**3.** Lithium (Li): A reactive alkali metal. It is the lightest metal and least dense solid element. Used to treat bipolar disorder.

**4.** Beryllium (Be): A toxic alkaline Earth metal. Used for radiation windows, it doesn't absorb X-rays and structural components.

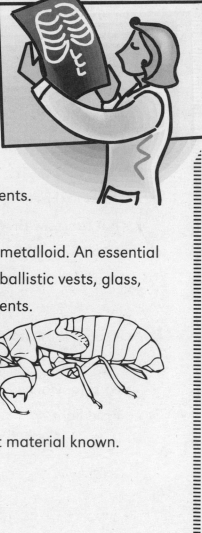

**5.** Boron (B): Black-brown metalloid. An essential plant nutrient. Used in ballistic vests, glass, insecticides and detergents.

**6.** Carbon (C): A non-metal. Essential for all life. Diamond form, hardest material known. Graphite is the only conducting non-metal.

**7.** Nitrogen (N): Colourless gas, a non-metal. Required for life, and in many explosive compounds such as TNT.

**8.** Oxygen (O): Colourless, highly reactive non-metal, chalcogen. Required for life. Used in smelting iron ore into steel.

**9.** Fluorine (F): A highly reactive toxic halogen, that reacts with          every element apart from Ne and He. Used in dental care.

**10.** Neon (Ne): A noble gas rare on Earth. Used in neon signs (obviously) to create a red light.

**11.** Sodium (Na): A highly reactive, silvery alkali metal. Essential for regulating blood pressure and pH. Used in making soap.

**12.** Magnesium (Mg): A strong, light, grey alkaline Earth metal. Essential to life. Used in cars, sharpeners, and hulls of ships.

**13.** Aluminium (Al): Another metal. No known biological role. Wide range of uses such as 'tin foil', construction and heat sinks.

**14.** Silicon (Si): Common metalloid. Found in sand. Eighth most common element in the universe. Used in most electronic devices.

**15.** Phosphorus (P): A non-metal. Essential for life, it is a component of DNA, RNA, ATP and bone. Used in fertiliser and matches.

**16.** Sulphur (S): A yellow non-metal. Essential component of life. Used as a fertiliser, fungicide and pesticide.

**17.** Chlorine (Cl): A highly toxic pale yellow halogen. Most common compound is NaCl, table salt. It was used as a chemical weapon in the First World War.

**18.** Argon (Ar): A noble gas. Third most common gas in the atmosphere. Used to store highly reactive materials and in lightbulbs.

**19.** Potassium (K): An alkali metal. Ions necessary for life, used in nerve transmission. It is used in fertiliser and gunpowder.

**20.** Calcium (Ca): A silver alkaline Earth metal. Essential for life, used in cell signalling. Also used in making cement, bones and cheese.

**21.** Scandium (Sc): A transition metal. Alloy with aluminium used in aerospace industry, baseball bats and bicycles.

**22.** Titanium (Ti): A lightweight, strong, transition metal. It doesn't play a role in the human body, but it is used in artificial hips and steel.

**23.** Vanadium (V): A transition metal. Used as a steel additive. Plays a more important role in sea-life biology than land life.

**24.** Chromium (Cr): A hard, transition metal. Used as a catalyst in tanning leather, and pigments. It has no known biological role.

**25.** Manganese (Mn): A transition metal. Used as a catalyst in the production of plastic, and steel production. Required for life.

**26.** Iron (Fe): A transition metal. It is the most common element (by mass) on Earth. It is essential for life and is found in blood.

**27.** Cobalt (Co): A transition metal. Essential for life, a key constituent of Vitamin B12. Used in batteries and to stain glass blue.

**28.** Nickel (Ni): A silver transition metal. Considered corrosion-resistant. Plays important role in micro-organisms and plants.

**29.** Copper (Cu): A transition metal with a high thermal and electrical conductivity. Used in wires, roofing and plumbing.

**30.** Zinc (Zn): An abundant transition metal, required for life. Used to galvanise iron or steel to protect against corrosion.

**31.** Gallium (Ga): A post-transition metal. No known biological role. Used in the production of semi-conductors.

**32.** Germanium (Ge): A hard metalloid. Used in fibre-optics, infrared optics and as a catalyst.

**33.** Arsenic (As): A very toxic metalloid. Used as a wood preservative and a leukaemia treatment.

**34.** Selenium (Se): A non-metal that rarely occurs in its elemental state in nature. Used in anti-dandruff shampoos.

SHAMPOO

**35.** Bromine (Br): A halogen. It is a red liquid. Used as a flame retardant and a pesticide. EtBr used to stain DNA in agarose gel.

**36.** Krypton (Kr): A colourless, odourless noble gas. Non-reactive, but does react with Fluorine. It is used in lasers.

**37.** Rubidium (Rb): An alkali metal. Highly reactive with air and water. Used in fireworks and PET.

**38.** Strontium (Sr): An alkaline Earth metal. Only element named after a town in the UK. Used in the study of neurotransmitters.

**39.** Yttrium (Y): A transition metal chemically similar to the lanthanides. Used in making phosphors in LEDs and in lasers.

**40.** Zirconium (Zr): A strong transition metal. It has no biological role, it is used for cladding nuclear fuel in nuclear reactors.

**41.** Niobium (Nb): A soft, grey transition metal. Used to make high-grade steel and super-alloys.

**42.** Molybdenum (Mo): A transition metal which is essential to life. Required for function of nitrogenase, an enzyme that fixes atmospheric nitrogen.

**43.** Technetium (Tc): A radioactive transition metal. It is the lightest radioactive element. Used as a radioactive tracer.

**44.** Ruthenium (Ru): A rare transition metal. Used to make water-resistant electrical contacts and as a catalyst.

**45.** Rhodium (Rh): A rare, hard transition metal. It is resistant to corrosion and its major use is in catalytic converters.

**46.** Palladium (Pd): A rare transition metal, that is similar to Plutonium. Used widely in organic chemistry for the Heck reaction.

**47.** Silver (Ag): A soft transition metal, it has the highest electrical and thermal conductivity. Used in photography and optics.

**48.** Cadmium (Cd): A soft, extremely toxic transition metal. Has many common industrial uses such as in batteries and photocopiers.

**49.** Indium (In): A soft post-transition metal. In its oxide form it is used as a transparent conductive coating on LCD screens.

**50.** Tin (Sn): A post-transition metal. Used mostly in solder and plating iron/steel containers for food preservation.

**51.** Antimony (Sb): A metalloid. Toxic, the effects of antimony poisoning are similar to arsenic poisoning. Mostly used as a flame retardant.

**52.** Tellurium (Te): A mildly toxic metalloid. With no known biological function, it is used in laser optics and semiconductors.

**53.** Iodine (I): A halogen which is a violet colour when a gas. It is essential to life. Used as disinfectant and as a catalyst.

**54.** Xenon (Xe): Colourless, dense, odourless noble gas. Can be used in photographic flashes, lasers and a general anaesthetic.

**55.** Caesium (Cs): An alkali metal. It is extremely reactive and pyrophoric (can ignite spontaneously). Used in atomic clocks.

**56.** Barium (Ba): A soft alkaline Earth metal. Never found in its pure form in nature. Used in X-ray imaging.

**57.** Lanthanum (La): First of the rare Earth elements and largest of the lanthanides. Used in Hollywood lighting.

**58.** Cerium (Ce): Rare Earth element and lanthanide. Used in self-cleaning ovens, yellow stained glass and lighter flints.

**59.** Praseodymium (Pr): Rare Earth element and lanthanide. Used in welders' goggles as it filters out harmful light to the eye.

**60.** Neodymium (Nd): Rare Earth element and lanthanide. Used in magnetics and green laser pointers.

**61.** Promethium (Pm): Highly radioactive rare Earth element and lanthanide. Not found in nature. Used in atomic batteries.

**62.** Samarium (Sm): Rare Earth element and lanthanide. Used to date samples from the moon and in nuclear plants.

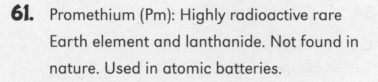

**63.** Europium (Eu): Rare Earth element and lanthanide. Used in CRT TV screens to give a red colour.

**64.** Gadolinium (Gd): Rare Earth element and lanthanide. Used as a contract reagent in MRI and found in computer memories.

**65.** Terbium (Tb): Rare Earth element and lanthanide, it has no known biological role. Used in lasers; its oxide used for colour TV tubes.

**66.** Dysprosium (Dy): Rare Earth element and lanthanide. Very reactive. Used in nuclear fuel rods as it captures neutrons.

**67.** Holmium (Ho): Rare Earth element and lanthanide. Has the highest magnetic moment of any known element.

**68.** Erbium (Er): Rare Earth element and lanthanide, which reacts with water and oxygen. Used as an amplifier of light in optical fibres.

**69.** Thulium (Tm): A lanthanide and rare Earth element, it is used as a radiation source in portable X-ray devices.

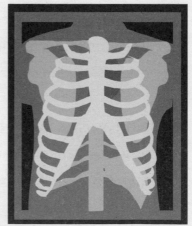

**70.** Ytterbium (Yb): Lanthanide and a rare Earth element. It is a soft metal and it can be used as a pressure sensor.

**71.** Lutetium (Lu): Lanthanides and a rare Earth element. Used for dating meteorites and radio-nucleotide treatment of cancers.

**72.** Hafnium (Hf): A silvery transition metal. Used in control rods for nuclear plants and in microprocessors.

**73.** Tantalum (Ta): A rare, hard transition metal. Used for capacitors in mobile phones, its oxide is used in camera lenses.

**74.** Tungsten (W): A hard, rare transition metal. Used as the filament in lightbulbs due to its high boiling point.

**75.** Rhenium (Re): A rare, heavy transition metal. Named after the River Rhine. Used in alloy form for jet engines and catalysts.

**76.** Osmium (Os): A hard, brittle transition metal, it is the densest natural element. The pure form can cause blindness.

**77.** Iridium (Ir): A hard, brittle transition metal which is the most corrosion-resistant metal. Can be used as a catalyst.

**78.** Platinum (Pt): A dense transition metal. One of the rarest elements on Earth and highly non-reactive. Used as a catalyst and in jewellery.

**79.** Gold (Au): A dense, soft, shiny transition metal. One of the least reactive elements. Used as a catalyst and in electronics.

**80.** Mercury (Hg): A heavy silvery transition metal, the only metal that is liquid at room temp. Both it and its salts are toxic.

**81.** Thallium (Tl): A highly toxic soft post-transition metal. Once used as rat poison. Used mostly in the electronics industry.

**82.** Lead (Pb): A dense, soft post-transition metal which is highly poisonous. Used for radioactive shielding and in batteries.

**83.** Bismuth (Bi): A post-transition metal which is very slightly radioactive. It has few commercial applications, used mostly in pharmaceuticals.

**84.** Polonium (Po): Highly radioactive metalloid. Discovered by the Curies and named after Poland. Used as trigger for nuclear weapons.

**85.** Astatine (At): Radioactive halogen. Due to its short half-life, the most stable being 8.1 hours, little is known about it.

**86.** Radon (Rn): Colourless, radioactive noble gas formed by the radioactive decomposition of other elements.

**87.** Francium (Fr): A highly radioactive alkali metal that decays into astatine, radium and radon. It is named after France.

**88.** Radium (Ra): An alkaline Earth metal, discovered by Marie Curie in 1898; it was used widely in cancer treatment.

**89.** Actinium (Ac): An actinide which can glow bluish in the dark because of its radioactivity. It is more dangerous than Plutonium.

**90.** Thorium (Th): An actinide named after Thor. It is three times more abundant than tin and is a component of camera lenses.

**91.** Protactinium (Pa): A bright, silvery actinide which is highly radioactive and highly toxic. It has no use outside of research.

**92.** Uranium (U): An actinide which is the last naturally occurring element. Used in nuclear plants and military ammunition.

*All the elements from element 93 (Neptunium), do not occur naturally on Earth and need to be made by man.*

**93.** Neptunium (Np): An actinide which is the first of the syntactically prepared elements. Can be used to create Plutonium-238.

**94.** Plutonium (Pu): An actinide which is incredibly dense and incredibly radioactive. Used in atomic bombs and some space craft.

**95.** Americium (Am): An actinide first made in 1944 at Berkeley. It is a soft radioactive metal and is found in smoke alarms.

**96.** Curium (Cm): An actinide first produced in 1944. It is a dense, silvery metal and highly radioactive. Named after the Curies.

**97.** Berkelium (Bk): An actinide first made in 1949 at Berkeley. It has no use outside of basic scientific research.

**98.** Californium (Cf): An actinide first made in 1950 at Berkeley. Used in machines to test for metal fatigue in aeroplanes.

**99.** Einsteinium (Es): An actinide discovered in the fallout of the first nuclear bomb test in 1952. Named after Einstein.

**100.** Fermium (Fm): The actinide discovered in the fallout of the first nuclear bomb test in 1952. It has no use as far as we know.

**101.** Mendelevium (Md): An actinide first made in 1955 at Berkeley by bombarding Einsteinium-253 with helium nuclei. Named after Mendeleev.

**102.** Lawrencium (Lr): An actinide first synthesised in 1961 at Berkeley. Named after nuclear physicist Ernest O. Lawrence.

**103.** Rutherfordium (Rf): Transition metal first detected in 1966 at Dubna by bombarding Plutonium-242 with Neon-22 ions.

**104.** Dubnium (Db): Transition metal first discovered in 1968 in Dubna, after which it is named.

**105.** Seaborgium (Sg): Transition metal first created in 1974 in Berkeley. Named after American chemist Glenn T. Seaborg.

**106.** Bohrium (Bh): Transition metal first synthesised in 1981 at GSI in Darmstadt, Germany. Named after Danish physicist Neils Bohr.

**107.** Hassium (Hs): Three atoms made in 1984. The team bombarded a lead target with iron-58. Named after the German state of Hesse.

**108.** Meitnerium (Mt): Made in 1982 by bombarding Bismuth-209 with nuclei of iron-58. Named after Lise Meitner, co-discoverer of nuclear fission.

**109.** Darmstadtium (Ds): Four atoms were detected in 1994 at a lab near Darmstadt, thus its name.

**110.** Roentgenium (Rg): Three atoms observed in 1994 in Germany. Named after Röntgen, a German physicist who discovered X-rays.

**111.** Copernicium (Cn): A transition metal, first created in 1996 in Germany. Named after Copernicus.

**112.** Ununtrium (Uut): First detected in 2003 in the decay of Uup. Synthesised in 2004. Only 14 atoms have been observed to date.

**113.** Flerovium (Fl): First observed in 1998. Named after physicist Georgy Flyorov. Most stable isotope 289, with half-life of 2.6 seconds.

**114.** Ununpentium (Uup): First observed in 2003, 50 atoms have been made since. Most stable isotope 289 with half-life of approximately 200 milliseconds.

**115.** Ununseptium (Uus): First made by a Russia–US team in 2010, a total of six atoms. Radioactive isotope 294, half-life of 78 milliseconds.

**116.** Ununoctium (Uuo): The last element in the periodic table. Only three atoms have been observed. It is radioactive.

# Periodic Table Scrabble

Use the symbols of the periodic table to make up words and phrases. Below are some examples.

## PLANETS AND MOONS

SUN

MoON

SAtURn

NePtUNe

URaNUS

CHArON
ErIS
CErEs
TiTaN
IO
OBErON
TeThYS

215

# ELEMENTS

CArBON
NeON
SILiCON
PHOSPHORuS
IrON
COPPEr

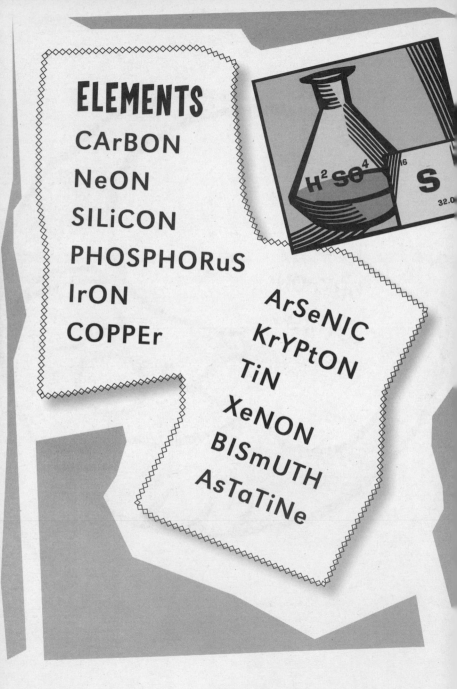

ArSeNIC
KrYPtON
TiN
XeNON
BISmUTH
AsTaTiNe

H²SO⁴

S
32.0

# FAMOUS SCIENTISTS

KReBS

WAtSON

CrICK

CAlVIN

KOCH

SALK

LiNNaEuS
(or LiNNE)

# THE WEATHER

AtMoSPHErIC PRessURe CAuSEs
CloUDs,
WINd,
ThUNdEr,
ICe,
RaIN,
SnOW,
MoRe PReCIPiTaTiON POsSIBILiTiEs.
NO SUN!

# OTHER STUFF

BaNaNAs CoNTaIN 'K';
'He' FOUNd In SUN;
'H' and 'O' In WAtEr;
Carbon-Holmium-Cobalt-
Lanthanum-Tellurium or
CHoCoLaTe

# Periodic Table

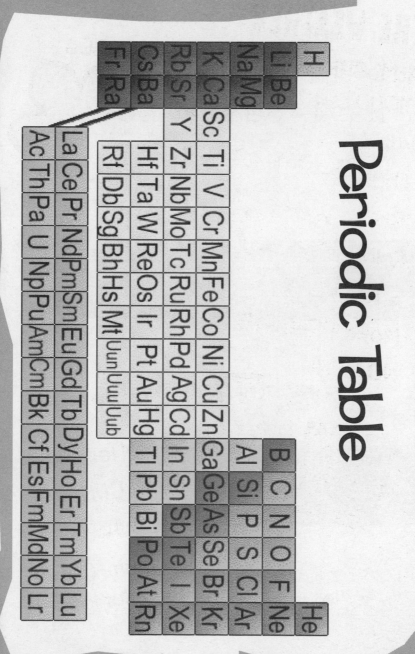

| H | | | | | | | | | | | | | | | | | He |
|---|---|---|---|---|---|---|---|---|---|---|---|---|---|---|---|---|---|
| Li | Be | | | | | | | | | | | B | C | N | O | F | Ne |
| Na | Mg | | | | | | | | | | | Al | Si | P | S | Cl | Ar |
| K | Ca | Sc | Ti | V | Cr | Mn | Fe | Co | Ni | Cu | Zn | Ga | Ge | As | Se | Br | Kr |
| Rb | Sr | Y | Zr | Nb | Mo | Tc | Ru | Rh | Pd | Ag | Cd | In | Sn | Sb | Te | I | Xe |
| Cs | Ba | | Hf | Ta | W | Re | Os | Ir | Pt | Au | Hg | Tl | Pb | Bi | Po | At | Rn |
| Fr | Ra | | Rf | Db | Sg | Bh | Hs | Mt | Uun | Uuu | Uub | | | | | | |

| La | Ce | Pr | Nd | Pm | Sm | Eu | Gd | Tb | Dy | Ho | Er | Tm | Yb | Lu |
|----|----|----|----|----|----|----|----|----|----|----|----|----|----|----|
| Ac | Th | Pa | U | Np | Pu | Am | Cm | Bk | Cf | Es | Fm | Md | No | Lr |

# What People Have Said About #Science140

Paul Lavin @plavin1922: 'Well this was fun. But I think I might have exhausted my fun fact repository!'

David Tana @Superoceras: 'Brilliant idea, just wish I'd caught on sooner!'

Laboratory News @laboratorynews: 'We loved the project – it's entertained and amazed us. And we can't wait for the book!'

Daniel G @Daniel_G666: 'Been fun, great work, great cause. Some interesting, confusing and funny tweets. Can't wait to see it finished & a 2nd edition.'

Stephen J Henstridge @HenstridgeSJ: 'It's been great. I've learned much – from other people's tweets (and a place to start further reading) and from researching my own.'

Lisa Darley @kookychemist: 'Really enjoyed reading the tweets. Look forward to seeing the book. Will be definitely getting a few copies for my classroom:)'

Eilis McGrath @NerdOdactyl: 'Well done to all involved – kept my twitter feed very interesting over the last while.'

Hellie Anseo @AnseoAMuinteoir: 'Loved it! Learnt so much :-)'

# Aoibhinn Ní Shúilleabháin

Aoibhinn Ní Shúilleabháin hails from County Mayo and has always held a fascination for science. An Entrance Scholar to University College Dublin, she graduated with first-class honours in BSc. Theoretical Physics and was delighted to take part in the CERN studentship programme at Europe's largest scientific research centre. Aoibhinn has taught mathematics, science, physics and applied mathematics at post-primary level for a number of years and is currently a recipient of the Ussher Award as a PhD candidate in Mathematics Education in Trinity College Dublin. She is also a Project Maths facilitator and Mathematics Pedagogy lecturer. Aoibhinn is a presenter of *The Science Squad* which looks at important scientific research underway in Ireland and has also enjoyed a weekly slot as the 'Daily Show Scientist', explaining the science of everyday phenomena on RTÉ1. Aoibhinn has worked enthusiastically with the Science Gallery Dublin for a number of years and is a member of their Leonardo Group.

Twitter: @aoibhinn_ni_s

# Maria Delaney

Maria Delaney is a native of the Laois–Carlow border, tipping just inside Laois and has lived in Dublin for a number of years. Science has always been her passion and she graduated with a first-class degree specialising in genetics from Trinity College Dublin. During her college career, she was the recipient of a Bill Vincent Award to work in Prof. Chenghua Gu's Neurobiology Lab at Harvard Medical School. As a Health Research Board Summer Student Scholar, she completed a project in Dr Aoife McLysaght's Molecular Evolution Laboratory. In June 2011, Maria set up a science blog, ScienceCalling.com. It was shortlisted for the eircom Spiders Mouth Award 2011, which looks for the most influential voice online in Ireland. Maria is currently completing an MA in Journalism at Dublin City University.

Twitter: @mhdelaney

# Humphrey Jones

Humphrey Jones is a science teacher in St Columba's College in Dublin. Throughout his twelve-year teaching career, he has endeavoured to bring science alive in the classroom, revealing science as an ever-expanding and dynamic field of study to his students. Central to this objective is the Frog Blog (www.frogblog.ie), a frequently updated website aimed at enthusing young people (and the general public) about the world of science and technology. The Frog Blog won the Big Mouth Award at the 2010 eircom Spider Awards and also took home Best Science Blog at the 2011 Irish Blog Awards. Humphrey is also a regular contributor to BANG, the *Irish Times*' monthly science supplement, and has also written for *Science Spin*, Ireland's dedicated science and discovery magazine. He is also heavily involved with in-service teacher training for the sciences, working with the Professional Development Service for Teachers.

Twitter: @TheFrogBlog

# Paul O'Dwyer

Paul O'Dwyer, a native of Cahir in County Tipperary, studied dentistry in University College Cork (UCC). While an undergraduate, his research on Enamel Microstructure was published in the *JIADR* and won the (All-Ireland) Crest Undergraduate Research Award. He was subsequently appointed Senior Medical Demonstrator/Tutor with the Department of Anatomy at UCC. Later, while working in general practice, his passion for health science education can be found in his newspaper column 'Word of Mouth'. As a Fellow of the Pierre Fauchard Academy, oral health promotion, dental science and communication are never far from his thoughts. A social-media enthusiast, Paul is an inveterate Tweeter. As a dentist, Twitter enables him to offer 'bite-sized' information to his followers. He hopes that the Science 140 project will help people 'get their teeth' into science! Paul is married with four daughters and lives in Nenagh.

Twitter: @ShirtNTie

# Acknowledgements

The Science 140 team would like to acknowledge the help and support of various individuals and organisations who have made this chirpy little book possible. First and foremost, we would like to thank everyone who contributed a #Science140 tagged tweet to the project. We received thousands of contributions over a three-month period and, unfortunately, were not able to include all of them in the book. *A Neutron Walks into a Bar ...* simply wouldn't exist without their efforts and enthusiasm.

We would like to pay particular thanks to a number of individuals who really engaged with the Science 140 concept, contributing hundreds of tweets each during its lifetime. These are Alice Sheppard, Dave Steele, Dean Burnett, Markus Hammonds, Michael Habib, Paul Lavin, Russell Dorman, Science Geeks (we never found out his/her real name), Stephen Uitti and Brian Goulet.

We would like to thank everyone at Dublin's Science Gallery for providing us with a place to work, an endless supply of coffee and great pizza. A noteworthy mention must go to Ian Brunswick and Fionn Kidney.

Thanks, too, to everyone at Hachette Books Ireland and also to the design team, who created a visually engaging book for all to enjoy.

We would like to thank our families, who were always supportive and willing to offer an encouraging word when needed. We would also like to acknowledge the wonderful support of our friends and work colleagues.

Finally, we are very grateful to the great folk at the Cystic Fibrosis Association of Ireland, our partnering charity. We are delighted that all royalties from the sale of *A Neutron Walks into a Bar ...* will go directly towards funding active research in the treatment and support of people with cystic fibrosis.

# Contributors

| Name | Twitter Account |
| --- | --- |
| 355/113 | @conorjh |
| Abie Philbin Bowman | @AbiePB |
| Adam Hill | @AstroAdamH |
| Adrian Vazquez-Perez | @uncletungsten |
| Alan FitzGerald | @FitzCamerons |
| Alec Speight | @AlecSpeaking |
| Alice Gorman | @drspacejunk |
| Alice Sheppard | @PenguinGalaxy |
| Andrea Barrett | @DrAndreaBarrett |
| Angela Alexander | @thecancergeek |
| annahalford | @anhalf |
| Aoibhinn | @aoibhinn_ni_s |
| Aoife McLysaght | @aoifemcl |
| Aonghus Ó hAlmhain | @aonghusoha |
| Azeeza | @krazeescientist |
| BenjaminGuy Saunders | @ThatBenjaminGuy |
| Beth Atkinson | @TheLandsBeyond |
| BHBS Science | @BHBSscience |
| Brian Goulet | @CapitainOmega |
| C Irregular Laurie | @choiceIrregular |
| Carol Cronin | @karlachameleon |
| Caroline Carson | @Conductor222 |
| Caroline Kidd | @caroline_kidd |
| Cathal Garvey | @onetruecathal |
| Catherine | @CatherineQ |

| | |
|---|---|
| Catherine Cronin | @catherinecronin |
| Catherine McGuinness | @CatsInTheMuseum |
| Ceehaitch | @Anonymoosh |
| Charming, The Prince | @RiezaApr |
| Cheryl L | @cowgirrl3 |
| Chris, allegedly | @psychworker |
| Christine Harkin | @MsHarkin |
| Ciara Ní Chionnaith | @CiaraMK |
| Ciara Ní Chionnaith | @CiaraMK |
| Claire Sweetenham | @drclairesweet |
| claireoconnell | @claireoconnell |
| Clodagh O Connor | @iamagnat |
| CMDoran | @TheFebrileMuse |
| Colin Wright | @ColinTheMathmo |
| Colm Ryan | @colm_ryan |
| cranntcd | @cranntcd |
| Damon | @Daanando |
| Dan Holden | @danrholden |
| Daniel Colquitt | @danielcolquitt |
| Danielle Barron | @MedEdHead |
| Dave Steele | @hullodave |
| David Connellan | @ConnellanDavid |
| David Curran | @iamreddave |
| David Jebb | @jebb_david |
| David Manly | @davidmanly |
| David O'Malley | @bendigodentist |
| David Pyle | @davidmpyle |
| Dean Burnett | @garwboy |

| | |
|---|---|
| Declan McGrath | @declanmg |
| Dermot Moriarty | @dermotmoriarty |
| Dermot Moriarty | @dermotmoriarty |
| Dulach Glynn | @DulachG |
| Eight Crayon Science | @8CrayonScience |
| Eilis McGrath | @NerdOdactyl |
| Emese | @EmeseH |
| Eoin Lettice | @blogscience |
| Fco. J. M. Guardiola | @guardiolajavi |
| Fiona Doris | @FionaDoris |
| Fiona Doris | @FionaDoris |
| Gina Allnatt | @gallnatt |
| Graham Love | @Graham_Love |
| Hanny van Arkel | @hannyvanarkel |
| Holly Kershaw | @cholly_ |
| Ian Sanderson Esq. | @iam_iam |
| Intel Ireland | @Intel_IRL |
| Introspection | @introspection |
| Ivan Leban | @IvanLeban |
| Jamie Condren | @JamieCondren |
| Jamie F. Lawson | @drlawson |
| Jamie Gallagher | @JamieBGall |
| Janette Ratcliffe | @Jet1577 |
| Julian Onions | @julianonions |
| Kallisti | @dancewithdoubt |
| Karen Masters | @KarenLMasters |
| Katie | @katiesci |
| Kees Engels | @KeesEngels |

| | |
|---|---|
| Krishaan1st | @Krishaan1st |
| Lali | @LalSox |
| Laura Meighan | @laurameighan |
| Lee Christie | @java7nerd |
| Liam Proven | @lproven |
| LifeScience Recruit | @ScienceJobs |
| Liz Nicholson | @ljrn42 |
| Louise Allcock | @DrShmoo |
| Love and Science | @BCFMLoveScience |
| Luke Solon | @lukesolon |
| Mags Amond | @magsamond |
| Maria Daly | @maria_daly |
| Mark Lorch | @Sci_ents |
| Mark Sexton | @SextonPhysio |
| Markus Hammonds | @InvaderXan |
| Mary Clare Higgins | @higma |
| Mary Mullaghy | @mmeureka |
| mchmiel | @mchmiel |
| Michael Barclay | @Gaiduku |
| Michael Habib | @aeroevo |
| Michael Plaice | @MlPlaice |
| Michael Seery | @michaelkls |
| MícheálJohnny | @MOMeachair |
| michelle cain | @civiltalker |
| Namnezia | @Namnezia |
| Ness T | @ceaselessness |
| Newstalk Science | @newstalkscience |
| Niall | @byrne_niall |

| | |
|---|---|
| Nick Cook | @nicholascook |
| notjarvis | @notjarvis |
| NOtoMagnetiteMining | @Pro_gaia |
| Orla Wilson | @orla_wilson |
| Paeds SHO | @PaedsSHO |
| Pam | @pamelaaobrien |
| Pamela Brophy | @PamelaBrophy02 |
| Paolo Viscardi | @PaoloViscardi |
| Patrick Denny | @draziraphale |
| Paudie Scanlon | @paudiescanlon |
| Paul Lavin | @plavin1922 |
| Paul O'Dwyer | @ShirtnTie |
| Peter Board | @PBCSciTutor |
| Peter Shum | @shump_2 |
| Raff Lab | @JRafflab |
| Reptile Facts | @ReptileFacts |
| Richard Lawson | @DocRichard |
| Roch Derilo | @rochryuusei |
| Russell Dornan | @RussellDornan |
| Sam Arman | @Samosthenurus |
| Science Geeks | @SciGeeks |
| Shaun | @shaunoboyle |
| Simon Watt | @SimonDWatt |
| Spotticus Giraffe | @SpotticusNH |
| Stephen J Henstridge | @HenstridgeSJ |
| Stephen Mulligan | @stephenmulligan |
| Stephen Prilliman | @SGPrilliman |
| Stephen Uitti | @suitti |

| | |
|---|---|
| Steve | @stevieL77 |
| Sucheta | @dreamyme |
| The Frog Blog | @TheFrogBlog |
| Thomas Kerin | @thomaskerin |
| Tim Wiles | @Timothy_Wiles |
| TriploidTree | @TriploidTree |
| TSV | @tattoosandbones |
| Twyeets | @twyeets |
| UCD Student Chapter | @UCDStudentChap |
| Vanessa | @astromad |
| Warwickshire Museum | @OisinTheDeer |
| Will Stanley | @w_stanley |
| Qawi Rabbini | @_Raqawi |